the very

web

Paul Carr

An Imprint of Pearson Education

London New York Toronto Sydney Tokyo Singapore
Madrid Mexico City Munich Paris

PEARSON EDUCATION LIMITED

Head Office:
Edinburgh Gate
Harlow
Essex CM20 2JE
Tel: +44 (0)1279 623623
Fax: +44 (0)1279 431059

London Office:
128 Long Acre
London WC2E 9AN
Tel: +44 (0)20 7447 2000
Fax: +44 (0)20 7240 5771
Website: *www.it-minds.com*

First published in Great Britain 2001

ISBN 0-130-41873-0

British Library Cataloguing-in-Publication Data
A catalogue record for this book can be obtained from the British Library.

10 9 8 7 6 5 4 3 2 1

Typeset by Land & Unwin (Data Sciences) Ltd, Northamptonshire.
Printed and bound in Great Britain by Biddles of Guildford and King's Lynn.

The publishers' policy is to use paper manufactured from sustainable forests.

contents

While the publisher and author have made every effort to ensure that all entries were correct when this book went to press, the internet moves so quickly that there may now be website addresses that don't work, or new sites we should cover. If you encounter any incorrect entries when using the book, please send us an e-mail at **oops@zingin.com** and we will make sure it is dealt with in the next edition.

The publisher and author can accept no responsibility for any loss or inconvenience sustained by the reader as a result of the content of this book.

introduction

Keeping in touch with friends, sorting out your finances, doing academic research, making holiday plans, shopping or just having a laugh – whatever you want to do, the internet makes it easier than ever.

There are millions of websites offering just about every product, service or piece of information you could possibly need. The difficult part is knowing which ones are worthy of your attention and which are just a waste of web space.

When we launched Zingin.com our aim was to create a user-friendly, UK-focused guide to the best of the web. Although both the site and the internet itself have grown massively since those early days, we're still dedicated to helping make sense out of the chaos.

With this in mind, when we decided to put this book together we were determined not to create just another huge list of websites – there are enough of them around and they just add to the confusion. Instead, we've tried to provide a user-friendly guide to the best of the bunch. From information to education, leisure to lifestyle, searching to shopping – if it's useful and relevant, you'll find it here; if it's not, you won't.

We've tried to make it as easy as possible for you to just dive in and get started with the book. The chapters have been put in a (hopefully) logical order, starting with news and information sites, then those which offer family-oriented information, then shopping sites and finally, if you still haven't found what you're looking for, there's a guide to the web's most useful search tools.

Although only the very best of the web has made it into these pages, we've headed up each section with **the best of the best** so you don't have to waste any time getting started. Also, if you know the name of the site you want, you can look it up in the quick reference section tucked away neatly at the back.

With the help of this book it should be pretty straightforward to find the information you're looking for but, if you do have any problems, make sure you come and visit us on the web (**www.zingin.com**) and we'll try our best to help you out.

Happy surfing!

Paul Carr
Founder
Zingin.com

news and weather 1

Ever since the Drudge Report (**www.drudgereport.com**) broke the Monica and Bill story before the 'proper' newspapers got a look in, people have been relying on the net to keep them up to date. Local, national or global – no matter how big the story, you can guarantee that it's being covered on one of our favourite news sites.

News portals

■ *The best of the best*

Newsnow **www.newsnow.co.uk**

A fantastically useful resource which brings together news from hundreds of international sources, all on one page. It even allows you to search a vast news archive for anything you might have missed.

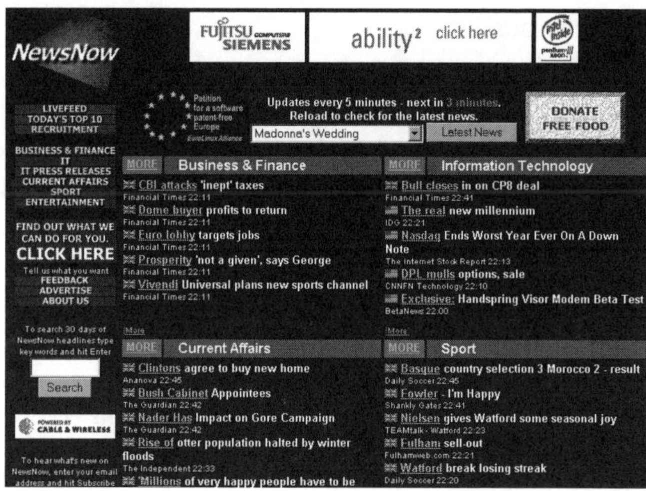

The rest of the best

The Paperboy **www.thepaperboy.com**

If you don't know the web address of your favourite newspaper or just want to browse over 4,000 newspapers from more than 150 countries then The Paperboy delivers all the answers. You can search by title, city, country and language or, to restrict your search to British titles, there's even a UK version (**www.thepaperboy.com/uk**). Although you can't actually search for individual articles from the site, it will certainly point you towards places where you can. For UK local newspaper content, also check out Fish4 (**www.fish4.co.uk**).

Moreover **www.moreover.com**

A bit like Newsnow but with more news sources and slightly more clutter. Worth trying for more in-depth news coverage.

Keep Ahead **www.keepahead.com**

Not enough time to read the papers? Simply sign up to this great service and the day's top stories will be delivered, each morning, directly to your mailbox.

UK news

The best of the best

BBC Online **www.bbc.co.uk/news**

If you've ever visited any of the BBC's websites you'll know what to expect here. Well-written articles are supported by video and audio clips, superb photography, external web links and much more – and it's all available in a huge searchable archive. First class.

The rest of the best

Guardian Unlimited **www.guardianunlimited.co.uk**

You don't have to be a *Guardian* reader to appreciate this excellent effort by the respected newspaper. Hundreds of articles are published online every day, and it's all stored in a searchable archive so you shouldn't have too much trouble finding something suitable. Well worth a look.

Electronic Telegraph **www.electronictelegraph.co.uk**

The *Telegraph* was one of the first newspapers to realise the potential of the internet, and its electronic edition should satisfy even the most news-hungry surfer. You'll need to register before you can read articles and search the archive, but it won't cost you anything and the quality and quantity of material is top-notch.

Sky **www.sky.com**

Sky laughs in the face of mere news sites with its complete information and entertainment portal. Take a packed lunch, you'll be here for a while. For more of the same, check out Teletext (**www.teletext.co.uk**).

■ *The best of the rest*

Independent **www.independent.co.uk**

Not quite up to the *Guardian*'s standard, but a great effort nonetheless.

Mirror **www.mirror.co.uk**
Tabloid journalism at its best, complete with a reasonably well-stocked archive.

Sun **www.thesun.co.uk**
The lighter side of the news? It's the *Sun* wot got it.

Times **www.the-times.co.uk**
Not the best of the online newspapers, but the *Times* site does include a huge archive and some nice web-only features.

International news

The Australian	**www.news.com.au**
El País (Spain)	**www.elpais.es**
Irish Times	**www.irish-times.com**
Le Monde (France)	**www.lemonde.fr**
CNN (USA)	**www.cnn.com**
Reuters (Global)	**www.reuters.com/news**

Weather

John Kettley is a weatherman and so is Michael Fish – and so, it would appear, is the internet.

■ *The best of the best*

The Met Office **www.met-office.gov.uk**
Not satisfied with providing up-to-the-minute weather forecasts, the Met Office also gives you access to satellite pictures, charts and climate information. Some official government sites can give you the impression that they've been thrown together in an afternoon, but it's obvious that the Met Office has gone out of its way to provide information in a clear yet comprehensive format. Outlook: bright.

■ *The rest of the best*

The Weather Underground **www.wunderground.com**
Continually updated forecasts and temperature information for the entire planet make this a great place to get a quick overview of the world's weather. Despite the

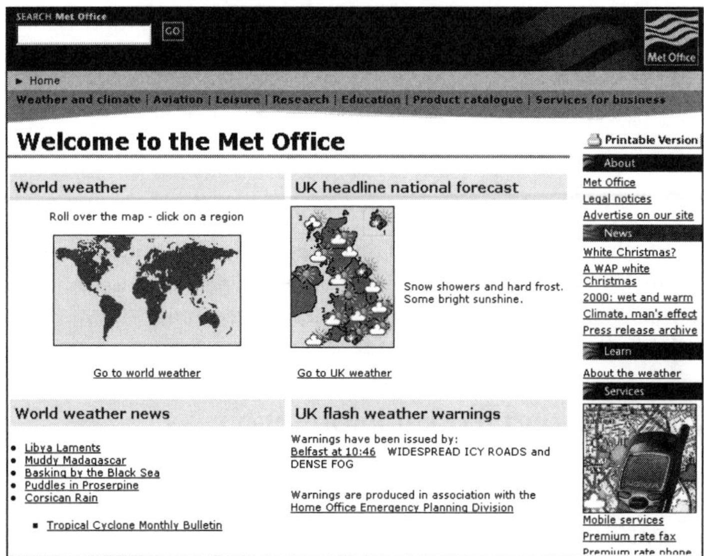

site's sinister-sounding name, it's not actually the headquarters of a group of renegade weathermen determined to overthrow the Met Office's evil meteorological dictatorship. At least, we don't think it is.

Yahoo! Weather **weather.yahoo.com**

Being an American site, Yahoo!'s emphasis is on the weather in Birmingham, Alabama, rather than Birmingham, England – but you'll find most cities in most countries covered.

2 money

No matter whether you're a multi-millionaire or a skint student, the internet makes it easy to make the most of your money, with banking, loans, investments, mortgages, pensions, insurance, financial news, economics, taxation and small business advice all just a mouse click away.

Financial news and market information

■ *The best of the best*

The Financial Times **www.ft.com**

No matter whether you want to check the performance of your shares, read the latest news on a particular industry, discuss economics with people around the

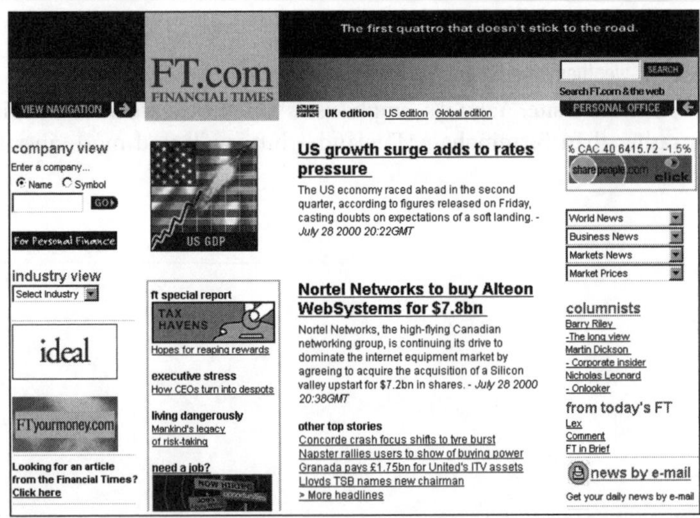

world or browse over 8.5 million articles from the world's top news and information sources, you'll find it all here – and plenty more besides.

■ *The rest of the best*

Yahoo! Finance (UK & Ireland) **uk.finance.yahoo.com**

Up-to-the-minute exchange rates, share prices, insurance quotes, interest rates and coverage of the major financial news stories are complemented by links to the UK's top money and finance sites, making Yahoo! one of the best places on the web to find financial information. If you're looking for in-depth features and plenty of gloss, you'll probably prefer The Financial Times – but for raw data, Yahoo! is hard to beat.

Money Guru **www.moneyguru.co.uk**

A relative newcomer to the web, Money Guru is already giving the big boys a run for their ... erm ... money. Concentrating on the markets, the site offers information and advice on the stock market, IPOs, global markets, funds and brokers as well as some busy topical discussion forums.

The Economist **www.economist.com**

Another site which needs no introduction, The Economist offers up-to-the-minute news, views and articles on all things economic. In addition to exclusive, web-only content, you can search the magazine's archive back to 1995, browse from your mobile phone and even download the suitably gripping *Economist* screen saver. A global success story.

Bloomberg UK **www.bloomberg.co.uk**

Bloomberg offers a goldmine of business news, market analysis, investment advice, interest rates, currency rates and pretty much everything else you need to watch the value of your investment fall as well as rise.

Gay Financial Network **www.gfn.com**

You'd be forgiven for wondering why on earth anyone would need a gay financial site. Well, although everyone spends the same money, regardless of sexual orientation, GFN realises that a lot of the traditional financial information on the web presumes that everyone lives in a traditional family group with a husband, wife and 2.4 children. If, heaven forbid, you didn't fit into that cosy pigeonhole then, before this excellent site came along, you were pretty much on your own. Now, thanks to GFN, everyone has access to information and advice suited to their particular requirements. Excellent.

Finance Wise **www.financewise.com**

No matter what type of financial content you want, this is a great place to start looking. Finance Wise is basically a search engine for money news, information and reports covering subjects from hostile takeovers to customer relationship management. A researcher's dream.

Money portals and information sites

■ *The best of the best*

This Is Money **www.thisismoney.co.uk**

This site, from the *Daily Mail*, *Mail on Sunday* and *Evening Standard*, may not be the most slick-looking financial information site, but behind the decidedly uncluttered front page lies a wealth of information on almost every aspect of personal finance.

Saving, investing, pensions, insurance, taxation and small business advice are all covered in impressive detail, with the emphasis on jargon-free, down-to-earth advice.

The rest of the best

FT Your Money **www.ftyourmoney.com**

Although the main *Financial Times* site is reviewed in Financial News and Market Information, the newspaper's personal finance site definitely deserves a special mention. Separated into your life, your opportunities and your decisions, each covering a range of subjects from education and employment advice to ISAs and insurance, FT Your Money will help you get your financial affairs organised in next to no time.

Money Extra **www.moneyextra.com**

The quest to inform strides ever onwards with this excellent guide to savings, loans, credit cards, mortgages, pensions and much much more.

Money Wise **www.moneywise.co.uk**

The online version of the popular *Reader's Digest* spin-off strikes an interesting balance between straight-talking financial advice and enjoyable lifestyle features. The usual blend of investments, pensions, mortgages and so on is complemented by articles on subjects like gardening, food and health, making for interesting reading even if you're not planning on signing your life away.

Children's Money World **www.childrensmoneyworld.com**

As the name suggests, this impressive site contains a whole world of money advice for ... erm ... children. Designed to teach youngsters the importance of money and its careful management, there's a family of cartoon coins, cross-curricular teaching material and plenty of advice on saving that pocket money.

Find **www.find.co.uk**

Don't let the slightly amateurish design put you off, Find is actually one of the most (if not *the* most) useful financial resources on the web, at least as far as UK users are concerned. The concept is simple enough – a directory of links to over 3,800 financial websites, categorised to make finding the one you want as easy as possible. Bookmark it now – you'll use it often.

Financial advice

■ *The best of the best*

Sort www.sort.co.uk

When you visit your local bank or friendly financial adviser, they'll offer you a cup of tea and talk you through your options without charging you a penny, but the minute you sign on the dotted line their commission starts to pour in. Sort takes a different approach, charging you a fixed fee for, say, arranging a mortgage or setting up a pension, but after that you don't pay them another penny. The success stories speak for themselves – £20,000 saved on an investment bond deal, £1,360 saved on a pension – silly not to, really.

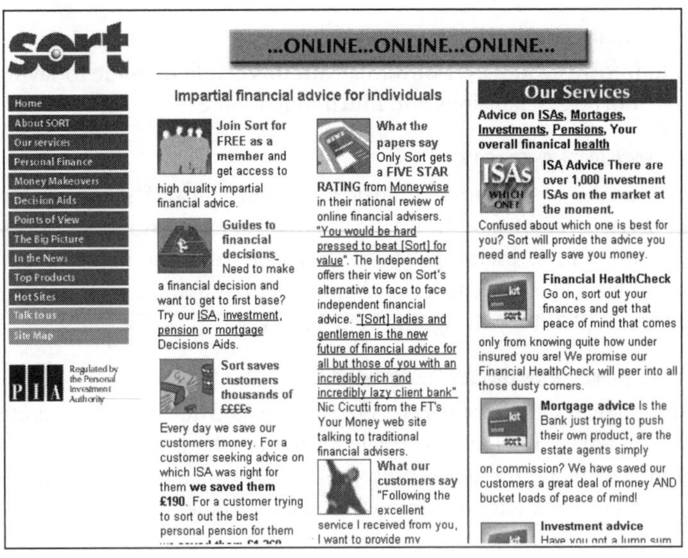

■ *The rest of the best*

Blays www.blays.co.uk

Blays is one of those sites which you've probably never heard of but once you've found it you wonder how you lived without it. In a nutshell, the site offers an extremely thorough guide to financial products and services, from credit cards to mortgages, complete with jargon-free explanations, comparison tables and everything else you need to ensure that you're getting the best deal for your money.

Moneynet **www.moneynet.co.uk**

Moneynet is one of those sites which make the internet so useful. No matter whether you're looking for a new credit card, a savings account, insurance or a mortgage, the site contains a complete run-down of the options available to you, how they compare with each other and, more importantly perhaps, how much you'll have to pay.

Buy **www.buy.co.uk**

Buy's goal is to take the hassle out of finding the best deal on services like gas, electricity, water and mobile phones, and it seems to be succeeding admirably. After you've answered a few very straightforward questions, you'll be given a list of suggested packages and tariffs from all of the major suppliers. If you like what you see (and you probably will), you can simply click the 'buy' button to order online.

Check Your Bank **www.checkyourbank.com**

According to Check Your Bank (CYB), overcharging by UK banks is costing customers £3–5 billion per year. That's about £3–5 billion too much as far as we're concerned and, if you agree, you'll be pleased to hear about this rather nifty service. Basically, you enter details from your bank statement and the site tells you if you've been charged too much by your bank. If you have then CYB will, for a nominal fee, help to sort things out – if you haven't, you can sleep that little bit better at night. Sounds good to us.

■ *The best of the rest*

Carpetbaggers **www.carpetbaggers.co.uk**

Making an easy buck just got even easier.

Investor Words **www.investorwords.com**

Over 5,000 financial terms fully explained to make sure you know your cumulative dividend from your custodial account. Suddenly all that small print makes perfect sense.

Banking

■ *The best of the best*

Gomez **www.uk.gomez.com**

First of all, we should point out that Gomez isn't actually a bank. Sorry. Instead, it's the best place to go to find out which of the online banks has most to offer in terms of reliability, service and cost – and, as such, is the only possible choice for our Best of the Best recommendation. Before you make a decision about which bank you're going to trust your hard-earned money to, simply visit the site and check out how your choice is doing on the Gomez scorecard. Oh, and it is into brokers, travel, shopping and car buying too. Splendid.

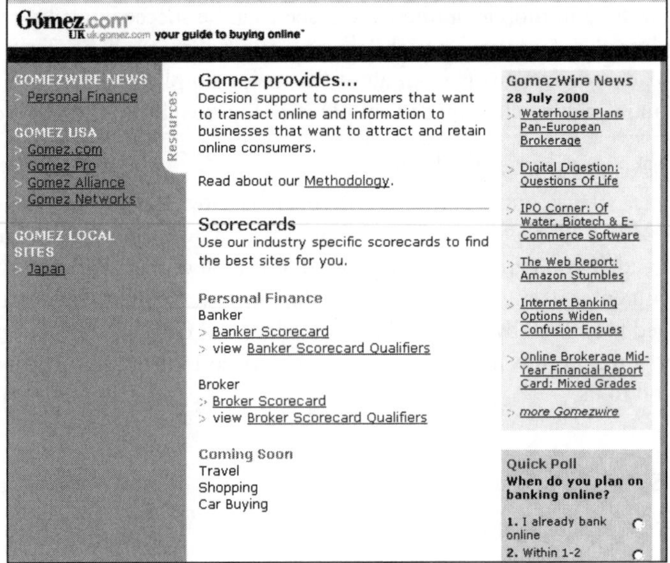

■ *The rest of the best*

Smile **www.smile.co.uk**

Forget queues, small print and frowns, Smile's website is all about Cheshire cats, pop art and Mr Men characters – and there's even some banking thrown in for good measure. The service offers completely secure account management, a silky smooth account opening process and a chequebook and cash card with a pink smiley face, plus, if you want to set up an ISA or apply for a loan, the site will tell you all you need to know.

Barclays **www.barclays.co.uk**

Once you've signed up to the Barclays service you can log into your account from any internet-connected PC – great news for office workers and students – and it couldn't be easier to transfer money, pay bills and generally sort out your finances.

first-e **www.first-e.com**

first-e was the first internet only bank to launch in the UK. No branches, no angry bank managers and (almost) no hassle. No matter whether you're looking for a savings account or a current account, you'll find a complete run-down of your options on this clutter-free site – and when it comes to actually setting up the account it couldn't really be much simpler.

Citibank **www.citibank.com**

Citibank may not be for everyone, but if you fit into the cash-rich, time-poor category then its excellent online banking service is well worth a look. All of the usual money management features are available, plus you can change your cash card's PIN, download account information for use with Quicken or MS Money, and even take advantage of some extremely useful money transfer features.

The Royal Bank of Scotland **www.rbs.co.uk**

You don't have to be Scottish to enjoy the online banking facilities offered by the Royal Bank. Paying bills, transferring money, viewing accounts and printing statements takes only a click of the mouse, and everything works at an impressive speed.

Cahoot **www.cahoot.com**

The next passenger on the 'my word we suddenly became cool' bandwagon is Cahoot from Abbey National. You know the drill by now – log on, sign up, pay bills, arrange loans, log off, go to bed.

For a complete run-down of all the major UK online banks, visit the Zingin Internet Banking Guide (**www.zingin.com/guide/info/money/banking**).

Loans

The best of the best

Money Extra **www.moneyextra.net/products/personal_loan_form.asp**

Why spend hours scouring the web for the best loan when Money Extra's excellent loan finder will do the hard work for you? Simply tell it how much you want to borrow and whether you're looking for a secured loan, an unsecured loan or if you have adverse credit, and with the click of a mouse you'll be presented with a list of options. Money Extra also provides the loan search features on Yahoo! Finance (UK & Ireland) (**finance.uk.yahoo.com**) – in case you were wondering.

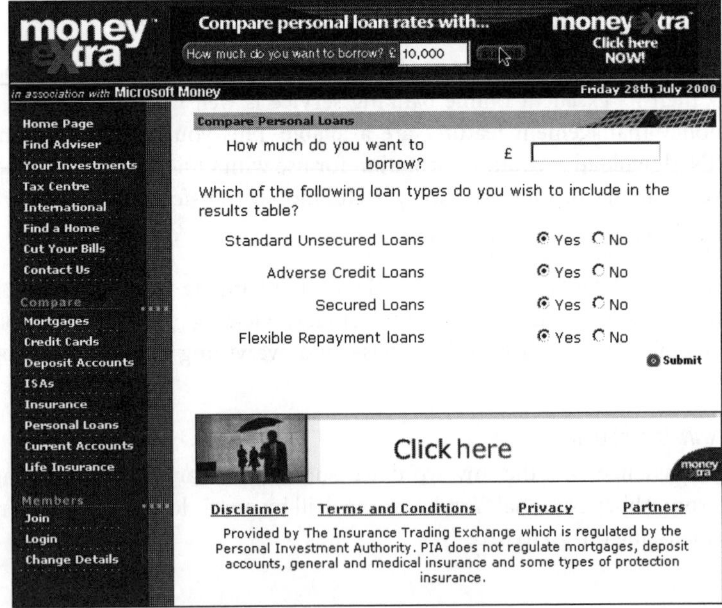

The rest of the best

UK Loan Search **www.ukloansearch.co.uk**

Rather than using an automated system, UK Loan Search uses real people (gasp!) to track down the best deal for you. The service is free but, even though they deal with 'over 150 lenders offering more than 4,000 different loan and mortgage schemes', they can't know everything, so it's important to shop around.

Credit cards

The best of the best

Egg **www.egg.com**

Simply visit Egg's site, tell them a bit about yourself and you'll be given an instant decision on whether you can have a card and, more importantly, how much credit you'll get. After that it's simply a case of signing a couple of forms (legal requirement, sorry!) and in a matter of days your shiny new Egg card will be nestling in your wallet. All of your billing, payments and balance transfers are handled online, and the rates aren't bad either.

The rest of the best

Marbles **www.getmarbles.com**

The real selling point here is the instant application system which, provided you're over 21, will give you an immediate decision as to whether you're special enough to deserve the card. Once (if) you become a card holder, you can manage your account, check your statement and even pay your balance, all without leaving your computer. A bit like Egg, only with fewer features.

Barclaycard **www.barclaycard.co.uk**

Barclaycard may not be as trendy as Marbles or Egg but it has an impressive reputation, you can apply and manage your account online – and, unlike the others, it actually has the word 'card' in its name. Nice touch.

Goldfish **www.goldfishcard.com**

Giant goldfish swim happily around this clutter-free site which allows you to apply for the card, manage your account and even redeem your Goldfish points for vouchers. Even if you don't want a credit card, just show the site to your cat and it'll be kept occupied for hours.

MasterCard **www.mastercard.com**

The official MasterCard site contains possibly the most useful of all the useless tools on the web – the ATM locator. Next time you need to withdraw some money, simply pop along to your nearest internet café or fire up your laptop (which you always have with you, right?) and find your nearest cash machine. For more of the same, check out Visa (**www.visa.com**).

American Express **www.americanexpress.co.uk**

It may not be the card of choice for many internet shoppers (or retailers for that matter), but this extremely funky, feature-packed site proves that at least it's making the effort.

Mortgages

The best of the best

Your Mortgage www.yourmortgage.co.uk

The usual mix of editorial and advice is available free of charge here, but the real prize-winner is the Mortgage Wizard, which makes it easy to search over 1,000 different mortgages to find the one that suits you. Simply answer a few questions and leave the rest to Your Mortgage. A no-frills site which could quite easily save you a fortune.

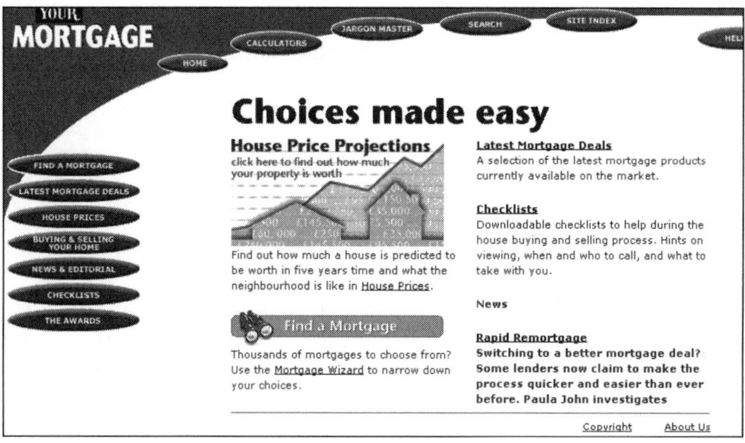

The rest of the best

Fred Finds Mortgages www.fredfindsmortgages.com

Fred, a cute character who desperately needs a haircut, is your guide to mortgages on this well-designed and extremely functional site. Once you've told Fred what type of deal you're looking for, he'll fly off and find the most suitable package from a number of leading suppliers. Behind the cartoonish design lies an extremely powerful system which will almost certainly save you a few quid on your mortgage. Nice work, Fred.

Just Mortgages **www.just-mortgages.co.uk**

Just Mortgages' design may be simplistic but the basic premise is the same as Fred Finds – you answer some questions and the site suggests suitable mortgages.

Charcol Online **www.charcolonline.co.uk**

John Charcol may not offer the largest range of mortgages on the web, but its award-winning site is super slick, offers some extremely reasonable rates and even has one of those clichéd photos of a call centre operator with a telephone headset and permanently set hairstyle. She's waiting for your call.

Council of Mortgage Lenders **www.cml.org.uk**

The official site of the trade association for UK mortgage lenders is a good place to go if you want to find out a little more about the standards you should expect from the industry.

Insurance

■ *The best of the best*

Screentrade **www.screentrade.co.uk**

If you want to find the best-value travel insurance on the web you can either waste hours trawling through the thousands of policies available or, alternatively, spend ten minutes letting Screentrade do the searching for you. Basically, you type in details of the type of cover you're looking for and the site will compare prices from the leading UK insurance companies to find the best deal for you – even allowing you to sign up online using a credit or debit card. Simple, but very effective.

■ *The rest of the best*

Rapid Insure **www.rapidinsure.co.uk**

Rapid Insure has obviously decided that insurance websites aren't cool enough and has set out to produce a suitably funky alternative. Behind the gloss, though, it's surprisingly easy to sign up for the cover you need, including travel, household, computer, pet and personal accident.

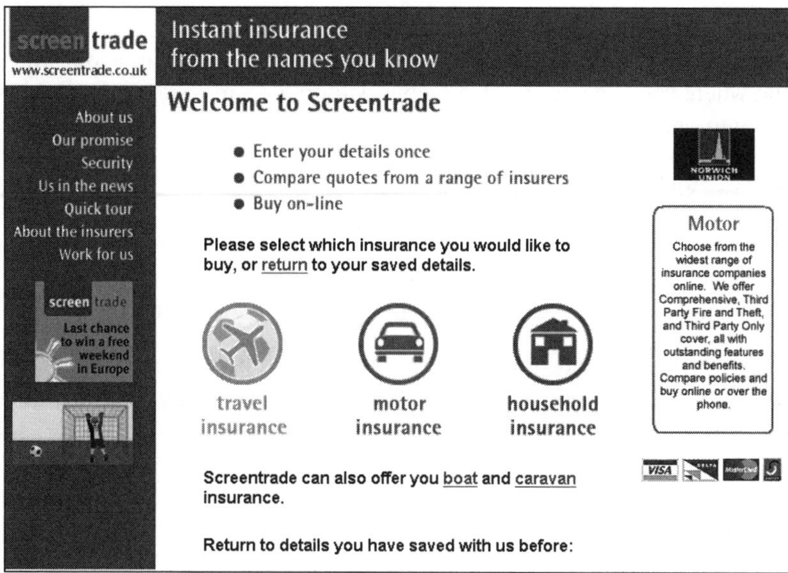

Eagle Star **www.eaglestardirect.co.uk**

Eagle Star is one of the few traditional insurance companies which have taken full advantage of the web to actually sell policies online rather than just giving a quote. Home, car, travel, life, even boats – whatever you want to insure, simply answer a few straightforward questions and, if you like the quote you're offered, you can seal the deal without leaving the site.

CGU Direct **www.cgu-direct.co.uk**

Despite a slightly jumbled navigation system, CGU actually offers an extremely quick and easy way to buy travel, motor and home insurance online. The quality of cover is some of the best we've seen, and the online ordering system is suitably straightforward to use. We like.

Direct Line **www.directline.com**

This bright and colourful site from the red car/telephone people allows you to get an instant quote covering your life, car, travel arrangements and just about everything else – and then sign up online. Nice.

Columbus Direct **www.columbusdirect.net**

How travel insurance should be done. Simply tell them a few details about who you are and where you're going, and Columbus will provide an instant quote and even allow you to sign up online.

NFU Mutual **www.nfumutual.co.uk**

You don't have to be a farmer to take advantage of the insurance services offered by NFU Mutual – but it probably helps. Travel, homes, cats, dogs, horses, ponies and even thatched roofs can be covered instantly, allowing you to get on with the important business of grumbling about cheap European food imports.

AA Insurance **www.aainsurance.co.uk**

While its rates may not be the cheapest in the business, the AA's motor insurance site makes it easy to find out what type of cover is right for you – and it's certainly a name you can trust.

BUPA **www.bupa.co.uk**

BUPA has an excellent reputation when it comes to providing health insurance services and, if the impressive quality of its site is anything to go by, you'll be in safe hands.

For a complete run-down of online insurance companies, check out the Zingin Insurance Guide (**www.zingin.com/guide/info/money/insurance**).

Pensions

■ *The best of the best*

Moneywise Pensions **www.moneywise.co.uk/pensions.htm**

Another triumph from the *Reader's Digest* folk. Moneywise Pensions provides loads of down-to-earth advice on the different types of pensions available, which one is best for you, where to go for more information, and just about everything else you need to know. A certain lack of depth at times, but there's more than enough to point you in the right direction.

The rest of the best

Scottish Widows **www.scottishwidows.co.uk**
Company news, information about the various products and services on offer and some annual reports and accounts (which only a shareholder could love) are complemented by downloadable application forms and the ability to invest in an ISA without leaving the site. Oh, and there's a picture of that woman in the cloak.

Scottish Friendly **www.scottishfriendly.co.uk**
Another pension professional with Scottish roots, Scottish Friendly's site looks very impressive but lacks some of the features which earn Scottish Widows and Moneywise Pensions a place on our Christmas card list. Having said that, if you want information about the company and the services it offers, you'll find it all here, so we can't really grumble too much.

Ins Site **www.ins-site.co.uk**
Ins Site offers not only pensions, but also handy sections dedicated to life assurance and remortgaging, if you like that sort of thing.

The Pension Site **www.thepensionsite.co.uk**
You haven't truly experienced the world of pensions until you've experienced The Pension Site. This industry portal offers up-to-the-minute pension news, special reports, appointment announcements, surveys and a useful contacts directory.

Investment information

The best of the best

Motley Fool **www.fool.co.uk**
From advice for beginners on how to trade effectively to intelligent discussion on the merits of different shares, you're bound to find something of interest here, regardless of your level of expertise. If you're new to stocks and shares and want to make sure that you're not backing a losing horse, it's a good idea to hang around in the discussion forums picking up tips from the pros – while if you really want the inside track, you'll want to pick up a copy of one of the site's wonderfully foolish guide books. Superb.

The rest of the best

Interactive Investor International **www.iii.co.uk**

This extremely impressive site specialises in price information for a variety of financial sectors, including shares, investments, pensions and mortgages. As well as the goldmine of constantly updated info, you'll find up-to-the-minute news and research, expert advice and even an online travel service.

UK Share Net **www.uksharenet.com**

It may not be the prettiest share information site on the web – but when it comes to the world of finance, looks most certainly aren't everything. At the top of every page there's a search box which allows you to find the current share price for your favourite company, either by name or epic code – and with performance graphs, regularly updated news, well-written articles and an impressive list of links to other relevant sites, there's plenty for everyone to see and do.

marketeye **www.marketeye.com**
Another one that's definitely for the expert, marketeye offers 'financial markets and investment information for the serious private investor'. While anyone can access time-delayed prices and useful information, if you want any more than that you're going to have to start spending some money.

Trust Net **www.trustnet.co.uk**
If unit trusts and OEICs are more your style, then Trust Net should definitely be your first port of call. The information is definitely not for beginners – in fact some of it looks like it needs to be read with an Enigma machine – but if you know the difference between your bid price and your yield, you can't help but be impressed.

Share Clubs **www.shareclubs.co.uk**
Small investors (in terms of financial commitment rather than stature) will love Share Clubs, which offers a meeting place to discuss strategy, swap tips, read the latest news and generally talk business.

Armchair Millionaire **www.armchairmillionaire.com**
The emphasis here is on getting rich slowly, with advice on savings, reliable investments, financial management and generally being able to look after your money better than you already do.

Global Investor **www.global-investor.com**
Forums, news, advice and books are complemented by useful guides to the world's exchanges and online brokers, making it a good place to go for an overview of a particular country's markets.

For a complete run-down of investment information sites, check out the Zingin Investment Guide (**www.zingin.com/guide/info/money/shares**).

Share trading

■ *The best of the best*

E*TRADE **www.etrade.co.uk**
Charles Schwab (see below) may be extremely popular but, for our money,

E*TRADE is just that little bit sharper. After your account is set up, you can start trading your hard-earned pennies on the stock exchange. Our only criticism is the slightly complicated pricing options but, having said that, it's no more complicated than the other sites – and if you can't understand the pricing, you're probably not quite ready for share dealing. It looks nice, too.

The rest of the best

Charles Schwab **www.schwab-worldwide.com/Europe**

Charles Schwab is one of the USA's largest online trading service providers and is slowly starting to conquer Europe as well. The service does pretty much everything you would want it to, and everything works extremely quickly. The registration process is straightforward enough and, after the legal stuff is taken care of, it's simply a matter of depositing some money in your account before you start gambling your life savings. If you need a second opinion, don't forget to check out the comparisons on Gomez (**www.uk.gomez.com**).

Barclays Stockbrokers **www.barclays-stockbrokers.com**

If you don't fancy trusting your money to one of those new-fangled internet companies, you might prefer the experience and trusted name of Barclays Stockbrokers. The real-time trading and fairly straightforward pricing policy is handy, too.

Sharepeople **www.sharepeople.com**

If you have ambitions to trade on the London Stock Exchange, the AIM, NASDAQ, NYSE and all those other acronyms the city slickers are so fond of, you'll definitely want to check out Sharepeople. Before you start trading you can sharpen your skills with a virtual portfolio – and once you're ready to get properly involved, the service offers some very attractive rates. Bright, colourful and a breeze to use.

iDealing **www.idealing.com**

iDealing manages to make the Barclays Stockbrokers site seem overly flashy, with plain text on a plain background and a simple text menu to navigate around the service. The pricing structure is one of the simplest in the business too, with a £10 charge for any real-time trade and, with a service this quick, you'll probably be making quite a few.

Self Trade **www.selftrade.co.uk**

Self Trade's trading system is no different from those of other companies, with instant online registration, followed by forms, followed by trading – but the emphasis here is on providing a service which is accessible to all. We like its style.

TD Waterhouse **www.tdwaterhouse.co.uk**

In addition to the usual mix of online dealing and price information, there's a constantly updated news feed, a handy company profile and all the advice you need to start trading.

Halifax **www.halifax.co.uk**

Much as we'd love to be cynical about the over-designed look of the Halifax site, its share dealing system is actually very impressive, with the option of trading online or over the phone, loads of market price information and news, watertight security and an interface that's extremely easy to use.

Deal4free **www.deal4free.com**

Deal4free offers online share dealing without any commissions. Yes, that's right, no charges for making your trade. How? Apparently Deal4free cover its costs by 'covering deals inside the market spreads' – which may or may not answer your question.

If you're still looking for a suitable method of trading shares online, don't forget to surf over to the impressive directory of brokers, advisers and more at Find (**www.find.co.uk/advice**).

Currency

■ *The best of the best*

Oanda **www.oanda.com**

There's a huge amount of foreign exchange information to be found here. If your interest in the world's currencies goes beyond finding out how much French wine

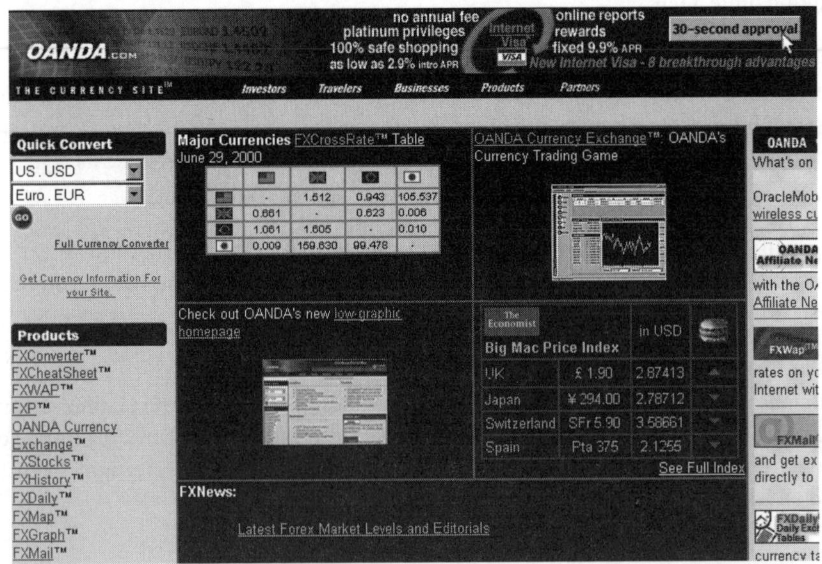

you can get for your pound you'll be spoilt for choice with news, up-to-the-minute rate information and even a currency trading game. Don't even bother with other exchange sites until you've been here.

The rest of the best

Thomas Cook Currency **www.thomascook.co.uk/currency**

Although it doesn't offer anything like as much information as Oanda, Thomas Cook's service allows you to order your currency online. Your money is delivered directly to your door and, when we tried it, there was no commission charge.

Yahoo! Foreign Exchange **uk.finance.yahoo.com/forex.html**

Quick and easy to use, Yahoo!'s foreign exchange tool does the job with the minimum of fuss. Simply tell it how much of which currency you need to change and click the convert button. Splendid.

Universal Currency Converter **www.xe.net/ucc/**

Although the UCC contains fewer features than Yahoo!'s offering, it's perfect if you're just looking for a quick foreign currency conversion. Simple but very effective.

Travlang Currency **www.travlang.com/money**

A useful service, designed specifically for travellers. Not only can you convert between most of the world's currencies, but you can also track their exchange rate history to see how much you could have got if you'd planned in advance.

The best of the rest

CMC Group **www.forex-cmc.co.uk**

'The world leaders in internet, share, Forex and derivative trading' make it easier and safer than ever to trade foreign currencies online.

Gen FX **www.gen-fx.com**

Gen FX offers a complete 24-hour online currency trading service, making it even simpler to lose large sums of money from home. Great.

Small businesses

■ *The best of the best*

Virgin Biznet **www.virginbiz.co.uk**

The main purpose of this site is to offer a way for small businesses to set up shop online quickly and easily by paying Virgin a monthly fee to build and maintain a website. However, even if you decide not to take advantage of Biznet's generous offer there's still loads to see and do on the site, including useful advice on running your business, discounts on products and services, a business locator to help keep an eye on the competition plus just about everything else you need to know to become the next ... er ... Richard Branson.

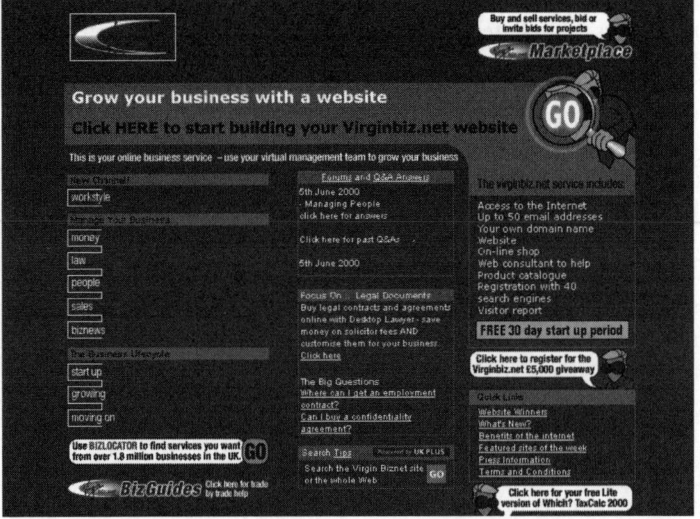

■ *The rest of the best*

Business Advice Online **www.businessadviceonline.org**

This official government guide to starting and running a small business gives you the low-down on taxes, trading online, government initiatives and employment, with useful guides and advice as well as links to other official information sources to help you keep everything legal.

E-Commerce Times **www.ecommercetimes.com**
If you fancy your chances as the next e-trillionaire, this is a pretty good place to start, claiming to offer 'everything you need to do business on the web'.

Altodigital **www.altodigital.com**
Aside from the debatable benefit of being able to set up a site for your business in 5 minutes – Rome wasn't built in a day using standard templates and a monthly charge – Altodigital contains a trading zone offering links to over 20,000 useful business products, businesses, news, franchise information, advice, links and so much more. Worth a look.

Entrepreneur Mag **www.entrepreneurmag.com**
This American site is a little gushing and 'self-helpish' at times but, with motivational stories and guides to expanding your business, there's enough information to get your entrepreneurial juices going.

The Prince's Trust **www.princes-trust.org.uk**
Younger business people will definitely want to check out this great source of help, advice and finance before taking those first entrepreneurial steps. It's got an impressive success rate, too.

Economics and taxation

■ *The best of the best*

Her Majesty's Treasury **www.hm-treasury.gov.uk**
News, the economy, government initiatives, ministerial speeches and announcements, every budget since 1994 and plenty more – it's all easy to find thanks to a surprisingly straightforward navigation system, and the noticeable lack of useless graphics makes the whole thing very fast to download. What more could you ask for? A tax cut perhaps.

The rest of the best

Inland Revenue **www.inlandrevenue.gov.uk**

The Inland Revenue are certainly not the most popular government department, but you have to give them credit for producing a pretty outstanding website. If you want to find out about what you have to pay, you'll find complete guides to income tax, tax credits, corporation tax, capital gains tax, petroleum revenue tax, inheritance tax, national insurance contributions and stamp duties.

Bank of England **www.bankofengland.co.uk**

No matter whether you're interested in banknotes or macroeconomics, you'll find something of interest here – with a guide to monetary policy, the low-down on the euro, educational material and just about every single document, bill, speech and forecast to affect the UK.

TaxAid **www.taxaid.org.uk**

TaxAid is a unique charity which offers free tax advice to people in financial need, promotes public understanding of tax and presses for a simpler and fairer tax system – an honourable mission, we're sure you'll agree.

Entitled To **www.entitledto.co.uk**

Entitled To, as the name suggests, is a free service which is designed to make it easier to find out how much help you can expect in the form of both benefits and tax credits. It is packed full of information and advice to make the whole process more transparent. If only the photographs on the site didn't show such grumpy people.

HM Customs and Excise **www.hmce.gov.uk**

With separate sections for business people and the general public, the official site of Customs and Excise is another prize-winner for the government's internet people. The sheer depth of information verges on the astounding, and if you're likely to be affected by customs or VAT, perhaps as an importer, an exporter or a business person, you really will find everything you need to know here.

Accounting Web TaxZONE **www.accountingweb.co.uk/tax**

The Accounting Web site is really designed for accounting professionals, but its excellent TaxZONE contains useful information for everyone interested in taxation. The information is, as you'd expect, a little heavy in places, but the expert advice, tax calculators and links to the best of the tax web make it well worth the effort. For more official taxation information, check out the Chartered Institute of Taxation (**www.tax.org.uk**).

The Euro **www.euro.gov.uk**

It may not have been updated for a while ('This site contains information for UK businesses adjusting to the reality of the euro in 1999') but The Euro site is still the best place to find the government's official line on the single European currency and to get a run-down of what it means for you.

3 home buying

We all know how stressful moving house can be. From buying and selling the house itself through to arranging a mortgage and telling everyone your new address, the entire process involves months of hassle and expense ... or does it? The internet may not have quite got its act together when it comes to finding your dream home, but it can still cut out much of the stress of moving and will certainly remove some of the leg-work.

Estate agents

■ *The best of the best*

Asserta Home www.assertahomes.com

Thanks to some big money from CGU and lots of high-profile advertising, Asserta

has leapt to the top of the tree with this extremely impressive virtual estate agency which offers property from thousands of 'proper' agents from across Great Britain. Simply type in your postcode, tick some boxes to outline your requirements and, before you know it, you'll be moving in to your new palace.

The rest of the best

House Web **www.houseweb.co.uk**

Boasting over 150,000 properties for sale, House Web is a great place to start looking for a new home – and with a guide to the web's finest home buying (and selling) resources you should have no problem finding what you're looking for. Lacks some of the gloss of Asserta, but then you shouldn't judge a site by its cover.

Bamboo Avenue **www.bambooavenue.com**

Phew! Just when we were starting to worry that silly site name fever had skipped the property market, along comes Bamboo Avenue to strike a blow for attempted coolness. The idea is not much different from the rest – to make it easy to buy and sell a house – but the presentation is a good example of what would happen if Gap designed estate agents.

Homes Online **www.hol365.com**

Lots of houses, tons of advice and links to removal companies, home news, home weather (?), utility companies and all those other things you need in order to get moving.

The best of the rest

Right Move **www.rightmove.co.uk**

'The home of home buying on the internet'. It looks good and works like a dream.

Where to Live **www.wheretolive.co.uk**

Where to Live may not have the overall shininess of Asserta or the number of homes of House Web, but if all the rest have drawn a blank, you've got nothing to lose.

Useful services

The best of the best

Up My Street **www.upmystreet.co.uk**

You can't fail to be impressed by the power and scope of this great tool, which allows you to find out everything you could possibly need to know about a particular area (by postcode) and even compare one area with another. If you're planning on moving house and want to check the crime rates, house prices, school league tables and council performance before you make a final decision, then Up My Street is a godsend – and once you've moved, it'll even help you to find your local pizza delivery company or painter and decorator. This is what the web should be about – to use it is to love it.

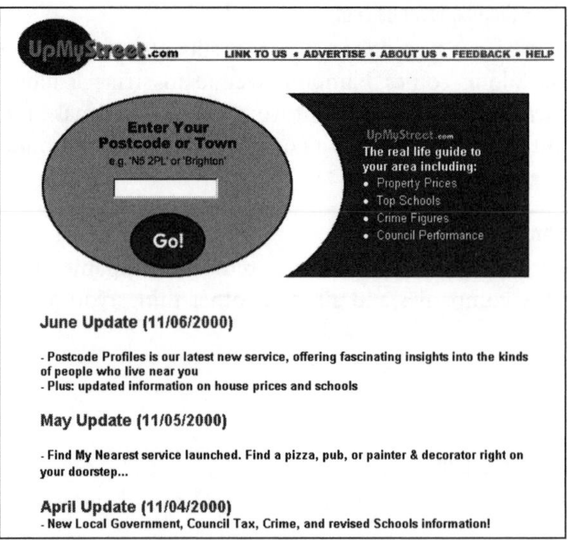

The rest of the best

Really Moving **www.reallymoving.com**

Really Moving is a veritable goldmine of information for anyone who's about to embark on the adventure of moving house. Every stage of the process is covered, including finding a house, arranging solicitors and surveyors, organising a removal company, moving in, home improvements and even where to buy electrical goods. In short, if you're moving house, this is an essential bookmark.

I Have Moved **www.ihavemoved.com**

I Have Moved is one of those services which is beautifully simple but absolutely invaluable if you're moving house. Very simply, you tell them when you're moving and they'll inform companies, utilities and friends that you have a new address. Now why didn't we think of that?

Proviser **www.proviser.com**

If you want to find out about property prices in your area then a visit to Proviser may well be in order. The design may be a little bland but, with easy-to-read price graphs for every area in England and Wales, it's extremely hard to complain.

4 employment

Just finished school, college or university? Made redundant? Stuck in a rut and looking for a new challenge? We've all heard stories about how good the internet is for helping you find employment – but with a huge number of recruitment and advice sites to choose from, where do you start? Luckily, that's where we come in.

Job hunting

■ *The best of the best*

Monster **www.monster.co.uk**

Thousands of jobs in a huge range of industries are available from the UK's largest employment site. As if offering a vast number of jobs in some of the UK's leading

companies wasn't enough, there's also plenty of help on offer – CV tips and tricks, interview advice and everything else you need to get the job you deserve.

The rest of the best

Gisajob **www.gisajob.com**

If you don't fancy the idea of trudging around the high street (or the web) visiting hundreds of recruitment companies then you'll love Gisajob, which allows you to search the job listings from over 5,000 agencies – all under one roof.

Top Jobs **www.topjobs.co.uk**

Another major player in the online recruitment world, Top Jobs lists positions in the UK and throughout Europe, allowing you to take advantage of the handy European freedom of movement thing, and also acts as official recruitment agent for some very well-known companies, guaranteeing you an excellent choice of jobs.

Stepstone **www.stepstone.co.uk**

Like many of the other recruitment services, Stepstone gives you the option of posting your CV online for potential employees to read and, with the number of companies actively using the site growing by the day, you'd be silly not to, really.

Hot Recruit **www.hotrecruit.co.uk**

Pack in your McJob and visit Hot Recruit for some of the most desirable jobs on the planet. We fancy a bit of wing walking.

Job Shark **www.jobshark.co.uk**

While most job sites seem happy to list billions of jobs in the hope that one meets your requirements, Job Shark offers a refreshingly targeted service. Simply tell them what you're looking for and leave the rest to them.

The best of the rest

Still looking? Don't give up until you've tried these …

Big Blue Dog	**www.bigbluedog.com**	Reed	**www.reed.co.uk**
Job Search	**www.jobsearch.co.uk**	Revolver	**www.revolver.com**
Jobs Unlimited	**www.jobsunlimited.co.uk**	Work Thing	**www.workthing.com**

Useful resources

The best of the best

About UK Jobs **http://ukjobsearch.about.com**

Finding a job just got a whole lot easier with this superb guide to UK employment. There's info on everything from accountancy to voluntary work, plus advice-packed articles to make the process as smooth as possible. Superb.

The rest of the best

I-Resign.com **www.i-resign.com**

Fed up with your job? Now it's easier than ever to resign with the help of the world's first resignation portal. This great-looking site offers advice on quitting, sample resignation letters, legal matters, discussion boards and even a hall of resignation fame covering a range of celebrity resignations in amusing detail.

CV Special www.cvspecial.co.uk

Although CV Special is basically promoting a business offering CV writing services, it also contains some very handy tips on what makes a good CV (and a bad one), advice on impact and covering letters, and everything you need to know to write your own glowing résumé.

One CV www.one-cv.com

One CV is a great idea, designed to meet the needs of anyone looking for a job on the net. Basically, the free service allows you to create an electronic version of your CV which potential employers can then access via the web using a username and password to guarantee your privacy.

5 law and public information

Legal advice

■ *The best of the best*

Law Rights **www.lawrights.co.uk**

If you don't mind paying a few quid for the privilege, you can get low-cost legal advice and documents to cover a wide range of legal issues on this excellent UK-focused site. Having said that, even if you'd rather not part with your hard-earned cash, there's still plenty of free information to give you an idea of whether a case is worth fighting or if you haven't got a leg to stand on. For more of the same, check out Desktop Lawyer (**www.desktoplawyer.freeserve.net**).

Law4Today **www.law4today.co.uk**

Forget high fees, amusing wigs and complicated jargon. Law4Today takes a more accessible look at the legal issues which shape our lives.

Find Law **www.findlaw.com**

Despite being based in the USA, Find Law is a great place to search for legal information, regardless of where you live. There's plenty of American information, which is obviously very little use if you're thinking about legal action in the UK, but if you dig deep enough, you'll almost certainly find what you need.

Trading Standards Net **www.tradingstandards.net**

Not only does the Trading Standards site contain a wealth of advice on consumer rights, safety and quality standards, but there is also a message board to warn others of your experiences and information on where to turn for help.

Politics and public information

■ *The best of the best*

UK Online **www.ukonline.gov.uk**

No matter what type of information you need, you'll find a direct link to the

relevant organisation, from local city councils and the monarchy to youth information and taxation advice.

The rest of the best

10 Downing Street **www.number-10.gov.uk**
News and information straight from the government. It's glossy and packed with information – but, basically, it's an electronic press release.

British Politics Page **www.ukpol.co.uk**
All about politics in the UK. Surprisingly enough.

The British Monarchy **www.royal.gov.uk**
Looking for the online home of the Royals? The gang's all here.

MI5 **www.mi5.gov.uk**
The name's Bond ...

There's a complete list of the major political party sites in the Zingin Politics Guide (**www.zingin.com/guide/info/law/politics**).

computers and technology 6

You probably won't be surprised to hear that the best place to find the latest computer and technology news and information is on the web. You may, however, be pleased to see just how much free information, advice and even software you can get for just the price of a local phone call.

Technology news and reviews

■ *The best of the best*

ZDnet **www.zdnet.co.uk**

News, information, downloads, reviews, gossip, competitions – whatever you need, it'll be in this massive internet and technology portal.

■ *The rest of the best*

The Register **www.theregister.co.uk**
UK-oriented technology news with a definite tabloid flavour.

Review Centre **www.reviewcentre.com**
Detailed yet clear reviews of the very latest in computers and technology.

VNU Net **www.vnunet.com/products**
Searchable archive of reviews from some of the UK's most popular computer magazines.

Wired **www.wired.com**
Internet news as it happens on this US-based internet and technology news site. As cool as geekiness gets.

Net Imperative **www.netimperative.com**
Up-to-the-minute news and information for the internet industry, focusing on investment, media, marketing and technology.

Slashdot **www.slashdot.org**
Packed to the rafters with unashamedly geeky technology news and gossip. This is where you'll hear it first.

Silicon **www.silicon.com**
It might be a bit 'industry' for some, but if you're looking for up-to-the-minute news on the business side of technology, you'll find articles, video reports and plenty more here.

Software downloads

■ *The best of the best*

Download.com **www.download.com**
Although there are thousands upon thousands of free downloads available here, finding the one you want is a breeze – simply choose your format, type in a few keywords and you'll be presented with a list of possible files. Once you find the one

you're after, it only takes a couple of clicks to start downloading it to your computer. You'll be pleased to hear that it's not all serious stuff either, with a huge number of demos for the latest games, many of which haven't even been released in the US yet.

■ *The rest of the best*

Tucows **www.tucows.com**

Tucows (Two Cows – you see?) is a slightly more funky version of Download.com, with a definite bovine influence. Not only can you search for freebies, shareware and demos, but there's also a software shop where you can download full licensed versions of popular software packages.

Win Drivers **www.windrivers.com**

Thousands upon thousands of hardware drivers are available here for download, sorted by product type and manufacturer – and although some of them are fairly large downloads, it won't cost you anything more than the price of a phone call.

Icons Plus **www.iconsplus.com**

In true *Changing Rooms* style, Icons Plus allows you to instantly transform your

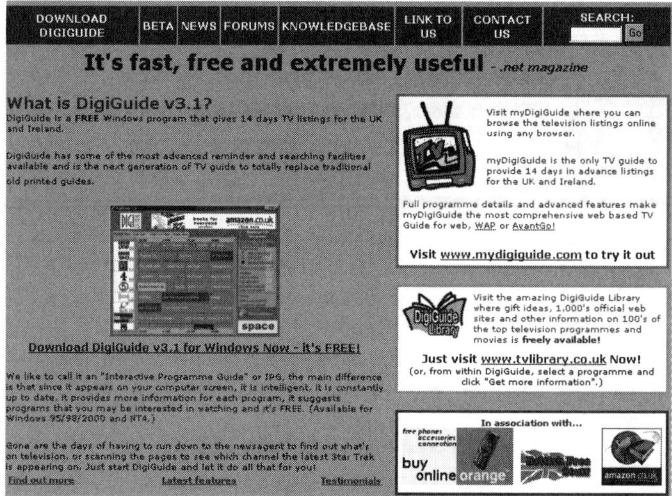

desktop into a chaotic mix of *Star Wars* characters, movie heroes, cartoon favourites and anything else that will fit into a little square. Good fun, but ever so slightly geeky.

WinZip **www.winzip.com**

Now that you've downloaded hundreds of games, printer drivers and R2-D2 icons, you need to uncompress them in order to install them on your computer. Your PC may well have come with a suitable unzipper, but if not you can get a very nifty one here.

Computer shopping

See the Electrical Superstores section in the chapter on Shopping for other electrical goods.

■ *The best of the best*

PC World **www.pcworld.co.uk**

Not satisfied with owning huge chunks of retail space around the UK, PC World has started its domination of the web with this surprisingly well-put-together site. Software, hardware, downloads and even furniture are available at (usually) the

same price as you'll find them on the high street – and the site's search system makes it easy to find what you're looking for.

The rest of the best

Micro Warehouse **www.microwarehouse.co.uk**

Computers, printers, software, mice and even some Mac stuff – every page of the Micro Warehouse site is packed with the latest technology at some pretty reasonable prices. Like PC World, the company has been around for years – so you should be able to trust them to look after you and, as it is part of the BT Trustwise scheme, your money is safe too.

Apple **www.apple.com/uk**

If Apple's glossy pictures and hip young models give you the urge to actually buy something, then you won't be disappointed – Apple's shop is one of the best, with fast delivery and the confidence that comes with buying direct from the manufacturer. Even if you're a die-hard PC user, you'll be tempted.

Dell **www.dell.co.uk**

Another company famed for selling its own products directly. Dell allows you to create your dream machine with as many (or as few) extras as you want. The prices are certainly not cheap, but the quality is almost legendary.

Evesham **www.evesham.com**

If you're looking for big brands like Packard Bell and Sony then you'll need to look elsewhere – but Evesham's own-brand products are reliable and affordable, so does the badge on the front really matter?

Gateway **www.gw2k.co.uk**

Once famous for using cows in its advertising, you can still see evidence of Gateway's bovine obsession dotted around its site. Cows aside, it's very simple to place an order – simply choose a system, decide on the specifications you need, and proceed to the checkout. No bull.

Elonex **www.elonex.co.uk**

Like Dell, Evesham and the rest, Elonex lets you customise your PC by adding or taking away until you're happy with everything – like very expensive Lego.

Software Paradise **www.softwareparadise.co.uk**
No matter whether you're a beginner, a business user, a developer or a fully fledged geek, there's something for you here – and if years of experience and plenty of happy customers aren't enough to convince you to buy, then look for the Which? Web Trader logo and the ISO9002 accreditation. Very nice.

■ *The best of the rest*

Computer Manuals **www.computer-manuals.co.uk**
No more clues.

Dabs **www.dabs.com**
Don't let the cluttered design put you off – there are some excellent bargains to be had if you dig deep enough.

Maplin **www.maplin.co.uk**
From processors to power supplies via monitors and screwdrivers – it's all here at prices that won't cause any headaches.

Ultimate Hardware **www.ultimate-hardware.co.uk**
When you're shopping for hardware, the last thing you want to do is wait hours for a complicated ordering system to load. Having said that, although the site is a little sluggish, the prices are pretty reasonable and it's all very funky.

Mesh **www.meshplc.co.uk**
Guess what? Yes, Mesh allows you to customise your PC to fit your exact requirements. Once you've recovered from that earth-shattering innovation, there is a more than adequate range of computer hardware and software to browse through.

Simply **www.simply.co.uk**
Still not tired of companies which let you customise your PC? Good news for Simply.

Viglen **www.viglen.co.uk**
… and Viglen.

communication 7

Welcome to free communication heaven! Postcards and e-mail, live chat and even free telephone and fax services – thanks to the following communication tools and resources, it needn't cost you the earth to keep in touch.

E-mail

■ *The best of the best*

Another.com **www.another.com**

If you want a free e-mail address which reflects your personality then you'll love the range offered by Another.com. After you've chosen your free address from the likes of *you@babemagnet.co.uk* or *you@thedigerati.co.uk*, you'll be able to send and receive messages from anywhere in the world. The huge list of available addresses means that you're bound to find something which sums you up.

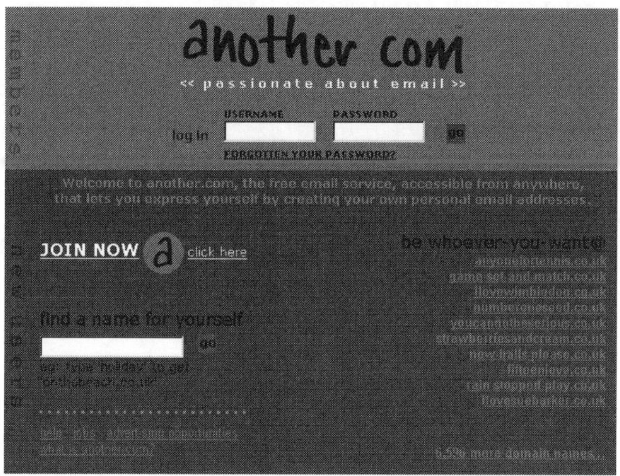

The rest of the best

Genie **www.genie.co.uk**

You'll never be worried about missing a message again with this nifty free service from Genie. Simply sign up for a free e-mail address and you'll be notified via your mobile phone every time a new message arrives. If that's not enough to satisfy your hunger for information, there's plenty of other useful stuff to be had, including news headlines and sports results. Functional and free – nuff said.

Hotmail **www.hotmail.com**

The mother of free e-mail services, Hotmail allows you to sign up for a free e-mail account which can be accessed from any online computer in the world. The only downside is that millions of addresses are already taken – so unless you are happy to be *a_very_long_name33@hotmail.com*, you might want to look elsewhere.

The best of the rest

Yahoo! Mail **mail.yahoo.com**

Yahoo! may have been the original search engine, but it's still playing catch-up with the long established Hotmail service.

Purple Turtle **www.purpleturtle.com**

It's not purple and there are no turtles in it.

Postcards

The best of the best

Egreetings **www.egreetings.com**

Thoroughly American greeting cards to let people know you're thinking of them. Avoid being overcome by some of the more sentimental cards by laughing yourself silly at gems like 'Happy National Hotdog Month'.

■ *The rest of the best*

Blue Mountain **www.bluemountain.com**

Avoid the cost of stamps and postal delays by sending your postcards by e-mail. Blue Mountain is the busiest postcard and greetings site on the web, offering a massive selection of free cards which are guaranteed to arrive home before you do.

Hallmark **www.hallmark.com**

This nice-looking site from the king of high street card shops offers some pretty funny cards in addition to the usual range of gooey sentiment. Well worth a look if Blue Mountain and Egreetings make you feel nauseous.

Keekaboo **www.keekaboo.com**

Keekaboo allows you to send a real postcard, delivered by a real postman, anywhere in the world for just a few pence. Ideal if you're travelling and want to make sure that your cards get home before you do.

Telephone

■ *The best of the best*

Contact Box **www.contactbox.com**

Billing itself as an all-in-one messaging solution, Contact Box should prove very useful if you want to keep in touch wherever you go. After signing up to the free

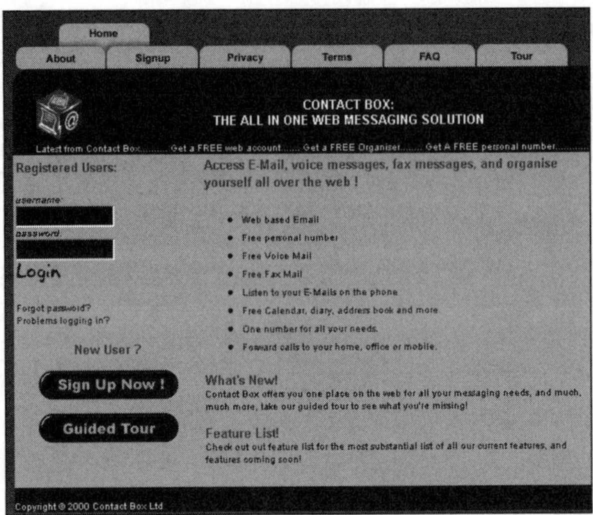

service, you are given a personal Contact Box telephone number which will forward your calls to almost any other phone in the world. If you're not going to be near a phone or you just want to get away from it all, Contact Box will even record a message and send it to you by e-mail.

The rest of the best

YAC **www.yac.com**

While not offering the same range of features as Contact Box, YAC does have some very nice call-handling features which will appeal to those who want a bit more control over their messaging.

International Dialling Codes **www.whitepages.com.au/wp/search/time.html**

Simply type in the name of the country you're calling from and where you're trying to call, and in seconds you'll have the correct code. There's not really much more to say, except that it works perfectly and it'll even tell you the correct local time.

travel 8

Making your travel plans online need not be any more stressful than, say, buying a book or a CD. Once you've decided where you want to go you simply find a travel agent, fill in a few boxes and you're off!

OK, it's not *quite* that simple – travel is an expensive business and there are billions of travel companies out there, each offering different packages, prices and options. To help you on your way, though, there are tons of sites filled with everything you could possibly need to make your trip a success, including country and city guides, currency converters, health and safety tips and even sun cream suppliers.

Portals and travel agents

■ *The best of the best*

A2B Travel www.a2btravel.co.uk

No matter where, how or why you're travelling, don't leave home until you've

checked out A2B Travel. A2B is the UK's largest travel information and booking portal. The layout may be a little cluttered for some tastes, but it only reinforces how much information is packed into the site. Whether you prefer to travel by plane, train or Eurostar, you'll find timetables, online booking and everything else you might need.

The rest of the best

Travelocity **www.travelocity.co.uk**

Behind the wonderfully cluttered front page you'll find a veritable goldmine of flights, hotel rooms, package holidays, weekend breaks and car hire. Tread carefully though, the prices offered aren't always the cheapest available, so it's worth checking Expedia, Teletext and the rest to make sure you're getting the best deal.

Expedia **www.expedia.co.uk**

The formula here is the same as for the other travel sites, with flights, accommodation and car hire – but the real prize-winner is the price comparison tool, which lets you find the best deal on your holiday.

Thomas Cook **www.thomascook.co.uk**

Not quite as impressive as some of the internet-only travel agents, but the high street giant does offer a wide range of package holidays which will particularly appeal to family holidaymakers.

Teletext **www.teletext.co.uk/holidays**

Teletext's holiday site offers some of the UK's lowest holiday prices – and you won't need to hunt for the remote control to find them.

Bargain Holidays **www.bargainholidays.com**

Fun in the sun without breaking the bank.

Brochure Bank **www.brochurebank.co.uk**

Save yourself the hassle of traipsing around travel agents. These folk will deliver brochures from the UK's leading tour operators direct to your door – free of charge.

The best of the rest

More useful holiday planning and booking sites ...

Air Miles	**www.airmiles.co.uk**
Airtours	**www.airtours.com**
Butlins	**www.butlins.co.uk**
Center Parcs	**www.centerparcs.co.uk**
Co-op Travelcare	**www.co-op-travelcare.co.uk**
Express Flight	**www.expressflight.com**
Holiday Discounts	**www.holidaydiscounts.com**
Lunn Poly	**www.lunn-poly.com**
Thomson Holidays	**www.thomson-holidays.co.uk**

Specialist travel companies

If you're just looking for a family holiday or a business flight then you're almost certainly better off with the mainstream companies – but if you're looking for tailor-made travel, look no further.

The best of the best

Lastminute.com **www.lastminute.com**

Specialising in impulse travel bookings rather than family package holidays, you'll

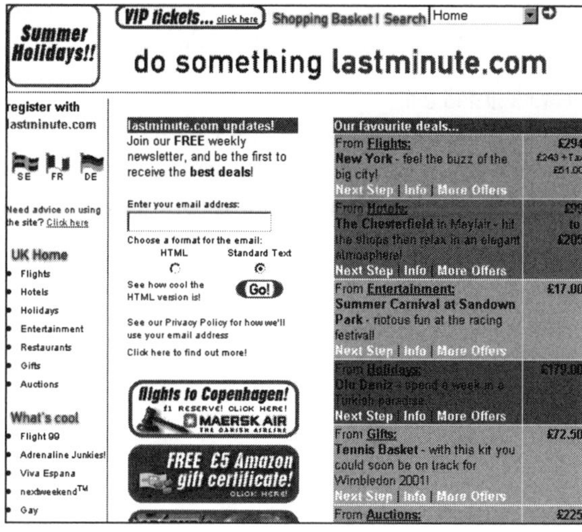

find some rock-bottom prices on European travel and accommodation. If you're the sort of person who worries about every detail when making travel arrangements then you might not feel entirely comfortable with this type of service as there's not much time to confirm your booking. If, on the other hand, you love to live life on the edge and/or on the cheap – make sure you leave it to the lastminute.

■ *The rest of the best*

Unmissable **www.unmissable.com**

Looking for a once-in-a-lifetime experience? Look no further. From unique music events to whale watching, there's something here for everyone.

Maximise **www.maximise.co.uk**

Specialising in short activity breaks within the UK, Maximise offers a huge range of activities – from paintball and karting to parachute jumping and white water rafting. Regular adrenalin junkies may also want to check out the Maximise Club (**www.maximise.co.uk/club**), which offers some excellent discounts.

Adventure Directory **www.adventuredirectory.com**

No matter what activity you want to do (heli-skiing?) and where you want to do it (Wanaka?), a quick search through this massive directory of adventure sports providers will get you on the right track without delay.

First 48 Network **network.first48.com**

Offering information, tours and guides for the traveller, First 48 is great if you're heading off the beaten track. No matter whether you want to book a trip to India or just check out which visas you need for Turkey, you'll find it all here. Also check out Trailfinders (**www.trailfinder.com**).

STA Travel **www.statravel.co.uk**

Already a firm favourite with students, STA Travel has created a suitably fresh and funky site which offers low-cost flights, overland travel and insurance services. You can make an online booking or use the site to find your nearest branch – there are over 250 to choose from. More at Campus Travel (**www.usitcampus.co.uk**).

Club 18-30 **www.club18-30.co.uk**

If you don't know about Club 18-30 holidays already then you probably wouldn't want to go on one. Sun, sea, sand and … so much more.

Saga **www.saga.co.uk**

Synonymous with high-quality over-50s travel, Saga offers holidays to pretty much anywhere on the planet. It has also recently branched out into insurance and other financial services.

Low-cost airlines

■ *The best of the best*

easyJet **www.easyjet.co.uk**

It's orange, it's bold and it's excellent value. easyJet, the web's favourite airline, offers low-cost flights aplenty whilst taking every opportunity to have a dig at BA. Great stuff.

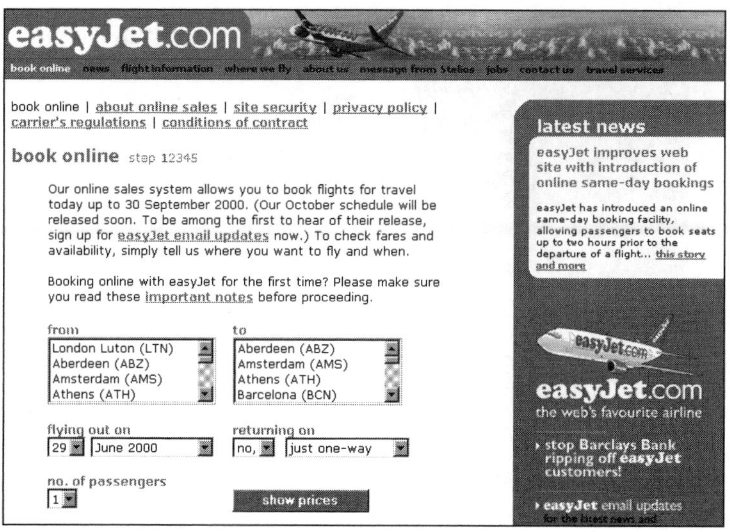

The rest of the best

Go **www.go-fly.com**
British Airways' low-cost offering has flights to a variety of European destinations. The service is ticketless, which means that once you've made your booking you can just turn up and ... erm ... go.

The best of the rest

buzz	**www.buzzaway.com**	Virgin Express	**www.virginexpress.com**

Full-fare airlines

The best of the best

British Airways **www.britishairways.co.uk**
Realising the benefits of internet booking, especially for business travellers, British Airways has built a very impressive internet arm. Its main UK site includes online

booking, special offers, flight times and everything else you could possibly need. Great, especially if someone else is picking up the tab.

■ *The rest of the best*

British Midland **www.britishmidland.co.uk**

Like BA, British Midland is certainly not the cheapest way to fly, but you can save a few quid on the site's occasional ticket auctions. The site itself is one of the better-looking airline offerings, with flight times, booking information and more presented in a clear way.

■ *The best of the rest*

Aer Lingus **www.aerlingus.ie**
Aeroflot **www.aeroflot.org**
Air Canada **www.aircanada.ca**
Air France **www.airfrance.com**
Air India **www.airindia.com**
Air New Zealand **www.airnz.com**
Alitalia **www.italiatour.com**
American Airlines **www.americanair.com**
Britannia **www.britanniaairways.com**
Cathay Pacific **www.cathaypacific.com**
Continental **www.flycontinental.com**
Delta **www.deltaair.com**
Eastern Airways **www.easternairways.com**
El Al **www.elal.co.il**
Finnair **www.finnair.co.uk**
Iberia **www.iberia.com**
Icelandair **www.icelandair.com**
Jersey European **www.jea.co.uk**
Kenya Airways **www.kenyaairways.co.uk**
KLM **www.klmuk.com**
Lufthansa **www.lufthansa.co.uk**
Monarch **www.monarch-airlines.com**
Qantas **www.qantas.com.au**
Ryanair **www.ryanair.ie**
SAS **www.sas.se**
Singapore Airlines **www.singaporeair.com**
Swissair **www.swissair.ch**
TWA **www.twa.com**
United Airlines **www.ual.co.uk**
Virgin Atlantic **www.virgin-atlantic.com**

Airports

■ *The best of the best*

A2B Airports **www.a2bairports.com**

The travel experts at A2B do it again with this indispensable guide to UK airports.

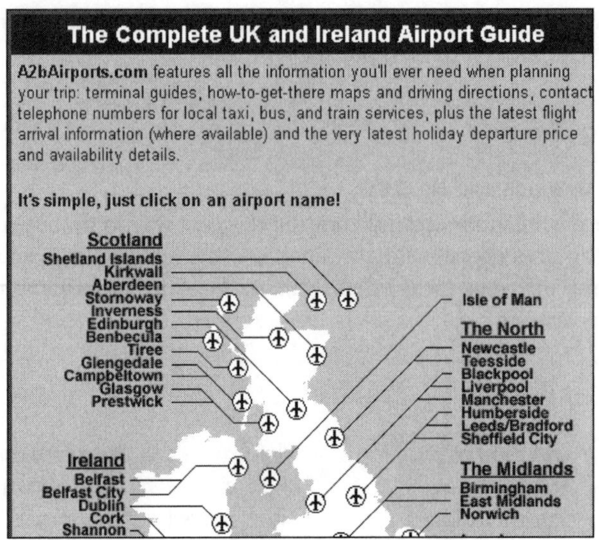

Flights arrivals, how to get there and other useful nuggets of information make this a must for travellers and plane spotters alike.

The rest of the best

British Airports Authority **www.baa.co.uk**

BAA provides a gateway to some of the UK's largest airports, including Heathrow, Gatwick, Stansted, Glasgow, Edinburgh, Aberdeen and Southampton. The most useful part of the site is the flight arrival information, but there's also a photo gallery and some pretty gripping airport news.

The best of the rest

Birmingham International	**www.bhx.co.uk**	Liverpool	**www.livairport.com**
Exeter	**www.eclipse.co.uk/exeterair**	London City	**www.londoncityairport.com**
Gloucestershire	**www.gloucestershireairport.co.uk**	London Luton	**www.london-luton.co.uk**
Isle of Man	**www.iom-airport.com**	Manchester	**www.manairport.co.uk**

Ferries and cruises

Nautical travel may not be as well represented online as flying, but the following sites should give you more than enough information to arrange your round-the-world trip or booze cruise to Calais.

The best of the best

A2B Europe www.a2beurope.com

Another winner from the A2B stable, providing information on ferries, seacats and more to help you cross the Channel with ease.

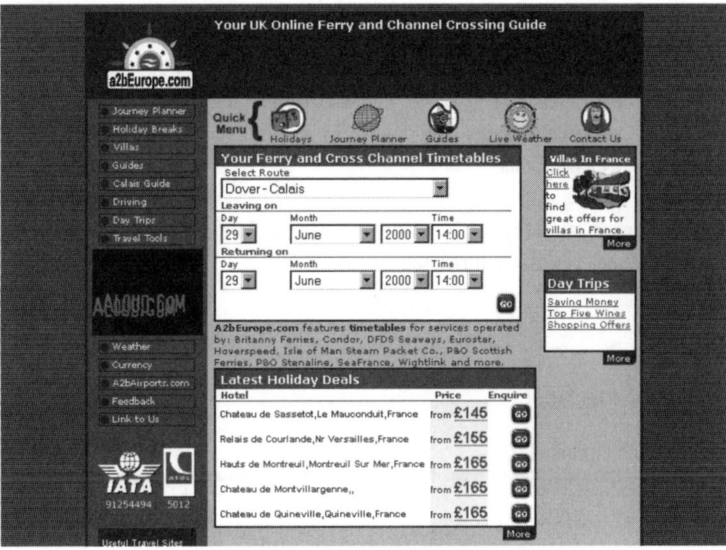

The rest of the best

PTI Ferry Information www.pti.org.uk/docs/ferry.htm

Providing links to most of the UK's ferry operators. Be warned though, some sites are much better than others.

Cruise View www.seaview.co.uk/cruiseview.html
Fancy a holiday on the ocean waves but don't know where to start? Everything you ever wanted to know about cruises but were afraid to ask. For ferries, check out Ferry View (www.seaview.co.uk/ferryview.html).

Boatastic www.boatastic.com
A massive range of boats and related products is available here at knock-down prices, allowing you to have as many cruises as you like without a sunset or game of desk quoits in sight.

The best of the rest

Brittany Ferries	www.brittany-ferries.com
Cunard	www.cunardline.com
Hoverspeed	www.hoverspeed.co.uk
Irish Ferries	www.irishferries.ie
P&O North Sea	www.ponsf.com
P&O Scottish	www.poscottishferries.co.uk
P&O Stena Line	www.posl.com
Red Funnel	www.redfunnel.co.uk
Sea France	www.seafrance.co.uk

For a full run-down of ferry and cruise operators, check out the Zingin Sea Travel Guide (www.zingin.com/guide/info/travel/sea).

Rail travel

The best of the best

TheTrainLine www.thetrainline.com
Save yourself the hassle of queuing at the station with this excellent site. Simply tell it where you want to go, what time you want to get there and what type of ticket you want. The site's booking system will check availability and allow you to book tickets instantly. It's easy to use and works like a dream.

The rest of the best

Railtrack www.railtrack.co.uk
If you just want to check train times without actually booking tickets, then

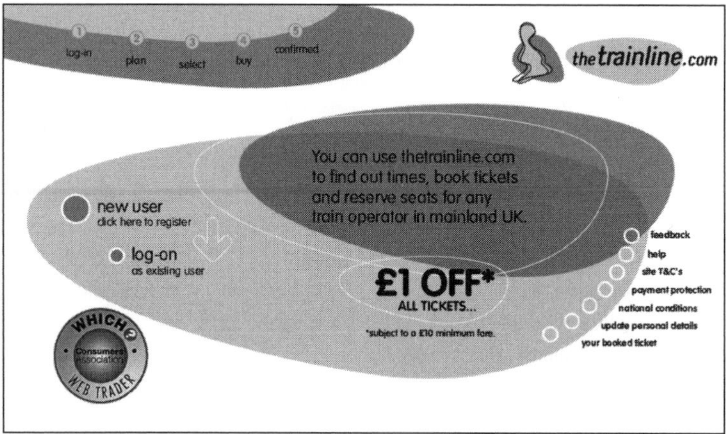

Railtrack's searchable timetable is indispensable. Also contains network information and a nice mix of news and corporate blurb.

Eurostar **www.eurostar.co.uk**

Not strictly speaking a UK train operator but certainly one of the better rail sites. Includes an up-to-the-minute timetable, travel guides and online booking. Très bon.

Chester-le-Track **www.chester-le-track.com**

Despite the site's slightly silly name (it's based in Chester-le-Street, County Durham), it contains a comprehensive set of links to a wide range of UK transport information. From train booking to obscure trivia, it's all here.

UK Railways on the Net **www.rail.co.uk**

Not the most attractive site on the internet, but it does contain a handy list of links to UK train company sites.

Rail Europe **www.raileurope.co.uk**

If you're planning on travelling around Europe by rail, you'll probably want to save a few quid with a discount rail card. Also offers low-cost Inter-Rail cards for students.

Rail Connection **www.railconnection.com**
Another nice-looking site offering discounted European rail travel.

■ *The rest of the best*

Central Trains	**www.centraltrains.co.uk**	Northern Spirit	**www.northern-spirit.co.uk**
Gatwick Express	**www.gatwickexpress.co.uk**	Orient Express Trains	**www.orient-expresstrains.com**
Great Eastern	**www.ger.co.uk**	Scotrail	**www.scotrail.co.uk**
Great North Eastern	**www.gner.co.uk**	South West Trains	**www.swtrains.co.uk**
Great Western	**www.great-western-trains.co.uk**	Virgin Trains	**www.virgintrains.co.uk**
Heathrow Express	**www.heathrowexpress.co.uk**		

Motoring services

■ *The best of the best*

The AA **www.theaa.co.uk**
Motoring heaven. This extremely well-thought-out site offers a very useful journey planner, traffic information and some excellent hotel and restaurant guides. The site is open to all, but AA members get exclusive access to a host of additional features and discounts. If you're not a member and are in the market for some breakdown cover, you won't be surprised to hear that you can sign up online.

■ *The rest of the best*

The RAC **www.rac.co.uk**
Hot on the heels of the AA comes this impressive site from the RAC which offers a route planner, motoring advice, online membership and plenty more. Not quite up to the AA's standard but well worth a look, especially if you're already a member.

Green Flag **www.greenflag.co.uk**
It may not be as popular as the 'big two' motoring organisations, but Green Flag has produced a site that's capable of mixing with the best of them. Here you'll find information about its range of breakdown services as well as a handy used-car checker.

Car hire

■ *The best of the best*

BNM Airport Car Rental Guide **www.bnm.com**

Quite simply, if you want to rent a car from the airport you'll want to start here. Despite being based in America, BNM offers up-to-date car rental rates, booking information and more for pretty much every airport in the world. If you're not leaving the UK and don't want to travel to your nearest airport to pick up a car, try searching for 'car rental' on Scoot (**www.scoot.co.uk**).

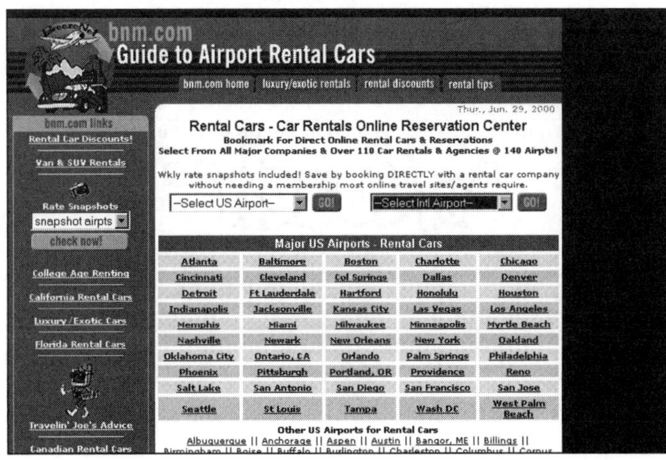

■ *The rest of the best*

If you need more information about a specific rental company or want to make an online booking, make sure you check out the following.

Avis	**www.avis.co.uk**	Kenning	**www.kenning.co.uk**
Budget	**www.budget.co.uk**	National	**www.nationalcar-europe.com**
easyRentacar	**www.easyrentacar.com**	Thrifty	**www.thrifty.co.uk**
Europcar	**www.europcar.co.uk**	U-Drive	**www.u-drive.co.uk**
Hertz	**www.hertz.co.uk**		

Coach travel

The best of the best

GoByCoach **www.gobycoach.com**

A nice move by National Express, which has created a site that allows you to book its services and also those provided by the other companies it owns. Almost all of Britain is covered – and judging by the prices shown, it is certainly a much cheaper alternative to the train. The site itself doesn't disappoint either, with a very useful timetable and online booking system.

The rest of the best

Wallace Arnold **www.wallacearnold.com**

While other coach companies take care of the day-to-day business of getting from A to B, Wallace Arnold offers coach tours to a range of UK and European tourist attractions. A very well-put-together site which makes coach travel fun. Almost.

Busweb **www.busweb.co.uk**

A must-visit site for anyone with more than a passing interest in coaches and buses. Busweb contains links to most of the UK's operators as well as keeping you up to date with the very latest coach and bus news. Gripping stuff.

Public transport

■ *The best of the best*

UK Public Transport **www.pti.org.uk**

This definitive guide to public transport in the UK provides instant access to a wealth of timetables, route plans, fares and much, much more. It's slowly improving the layout, but UK Public Transport remains a superb example of content over style.

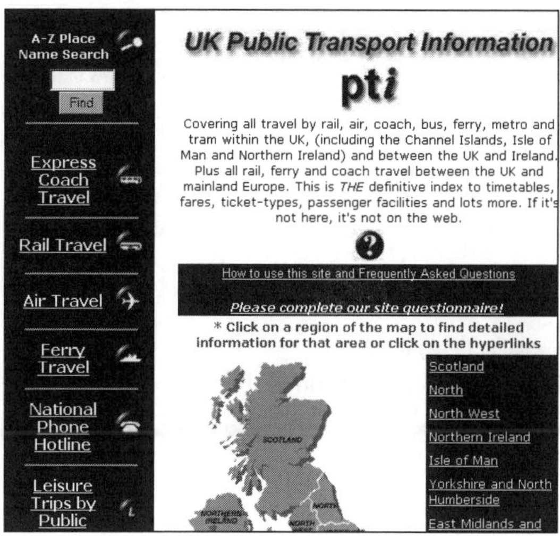

■ *The rest of the best*

Transport for London **www.londontransport.co.uk**

Travelling around our nation's capital can be a stressful affair at the best of times. The official Transport for London site has some very handy features, including a downloadable underground map and a list of bus routes – but, appropriately enough, it still needs a bit of work.

Tube Hell **www.tubehell.com**

Tube Hell is a site dedicated to complaining about how unreliable, dirty and just plain bad the London Underground is, with stories of nightmare journeys aplenty. If you're one of London's thousands of tube sardines – this one's for you!

■ *The best of the rest*

Public transport operators have been amazingly slow to take advantage of the internet as a marketing and information tool, perhaps because many of them don't have to fight too hard for customers. At least you can be safe in the knowledge that although you'll wait for ages for someone to create a decent site, two will probably come along at once.

Arriva	**www.arriva.co.uk**	Oxford Bus	**www.oxfordbus.co.uk**
First Group	**www.firstgroup.com**	Scottish Citylink	**www.citylink.co.uk**
Green Line	**www.greenline.co.uk**	Stagecoach	**www.stagecoachholdings.com**

Hotels

■ *The best of the best*

AA Hotel Finder **www.theaa.co.uk/hotels**

Over 8,000 UK hotels listed and rated by the AA, allowing you to choose accommodation with confidence. If nothing appeals, the RAC offers a similar service at **www.rac.co.uk/services/hotelfinder.**

■ *The rest of the best*

Leisure Planet **www.leisureplanet.com**

A massive resource containing photographs and information for over 50,000 hotels around the world. If you can't find something suitable here then you're probably too fussy to go on holiday anyway.

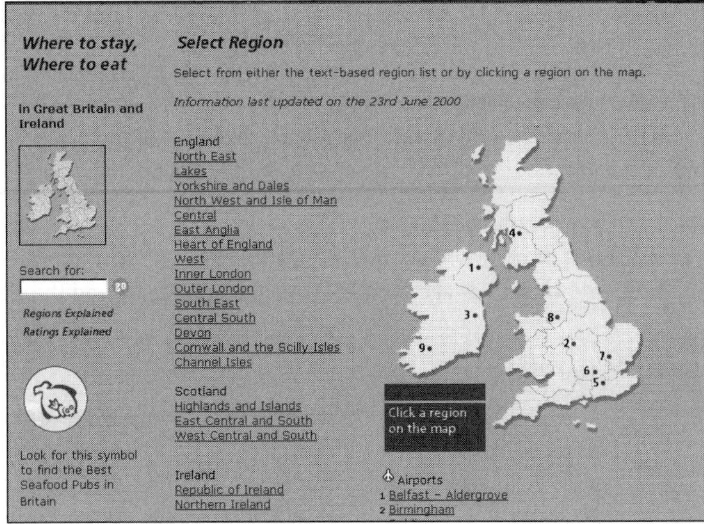

Places to Stay **www.placestostay.com**

Places to Stay brings together a huge variety of international hotels, with a very straightforward search system to find the one which best meets your requirements. This useful resource allows you to make an instant online booking and is an absolute godsend for business travellers.

Leisure Hunt **www.leisurehunt.com**

Another triumph of content over design. Search for a hotel or guesthouse anywhere in the world by location, price or facilities. The design is far from inspiring, but the depth of information will certainly bring a smile to your face.

Infotel **www.infotel.co.uk**

Comprehensive database of UK hotels and guesthouses, with location information, ratings and a booking system. Not the easiest site to use, but very useful nonetheless.

Late Rooms **www.laterooms.com**

If you're staying in the UK and have left it a bit late to arrange a hotel, you'll certainly want to check out the last-minute bargains available from Late Rooms.

This well-laid-out site should have something that fits the bill, but if you have no luck don't forget to try Lastminute.com (**www.lastminute.com**).

Holiday Rentals **www.holiday-rentals.co.uk**
Whether you're travelling in Scotland or St Lucia, this site will help you find your home from home.

Home Exchange **www.homeexchange.com**
Don't pay for a hotel abroad when you can just swap houses with someone who lives there. Plenty of houses, cottages and apartments on offer around the world.

The best of the rest

Forte	**www.forte-hotels.com**
Four Seasons	**www.fourseasons.com**
Gleneagles	**www.gleneagles.com**
Hilton	**www.hilton.co.uk**
Intercontinental	**www.interconti.com**
Lanesborough	**www.lanesborough.com**
MacDonald	**www.macdonaldhotels.co.uk**
Mandarin Oriental	**www.mandarin-oriental.com**
Marriott	**www.marriott.com**
Moat House Hotels	**www.moathousehotels.com**
Novotel	**www.novotel.com**
Orient Express	**www.orient-expresshotels.com**
Queens Moat	**www.queensmoat.com**
Ritz	**www.theritzhotel.co.uk**
Savoy Group	**www.savoy-group.co.uk**
Swallow	**www.swallowhotels.com**
Thistle Hotels	**www.thistlehotels.com**
Travelodge	**www.travelodge.co.uk**

Hostels and campsites

The best of the best

Hostels.com **www.hostels.com**
Comprehensive independent listing of hostels around the world, backed up with some very well-written advice for travellers. An absolute life-saver if you're travelling on a budget and need a bed for the night.

The rest of the best

Eurotrip **www.eurotrip.com**
As the name suggests, this is a resource for travellers around Europe. In addition to

a useful (although far from complete) hostel listing, you'll find a range of articles, advice and links to help you on your way.

UK Sites **www.uk-sites.com**

The design and layout may leave a little to be desired, but it's hard to fault the content. Over 2,250 campsites are currently listed, with more being added all the time. Simply choose a county for a full list of campsites and caravan parks, along with a contact phone number and postcode.

Hostelling International **www.yha.org.uk**

Representing over 4,500 hostels in over 60 countries, this nice-looking site also allows you to apply for a discount card to save even more money.

ABC Camping **www.abccamping.com**

All the information you need to arrange a camping holiday in France. It's what all those school French lessons were for.

■ *The best of the rest*

The Traveller (Caravanning) **www.thetraveller.co.uk**

Leading the way for caravanning on the world wide web. Enough said.

UK Caravan Parks and Campsites **www.ukparks.com**
The British Holiday and Home Parks Association site allows you to find your nearest caravan park, campsite or chalet across the UK.

World guides

■ *The best of the best*

Fodors **www.fodors.com**
Covering the world's most popular destinations, Fodors offer information on the best places to see, eat and stay, along with well-researched advice for the first-time visitor. Beautifully written, well researched – this is one travel site you won't want to leave.

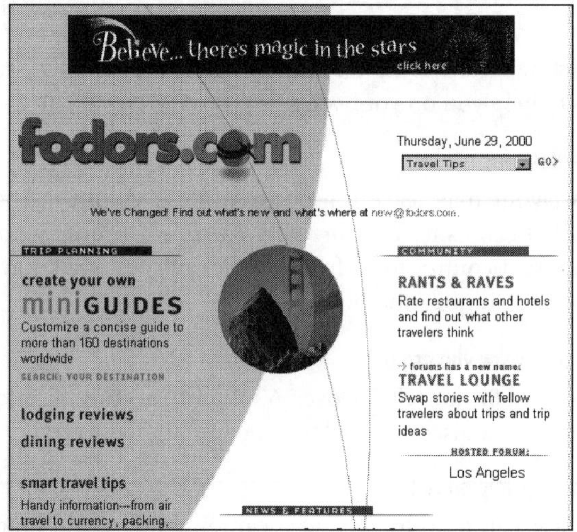

■ *The rest of the best*

Rough Guides **travel.roughguides.com**
A worthy challenger to Fodors for the title of best backpacker travel site. Rough Guides has been kind enough to publish the entire contents of its books on the web,

allowing you to get a feel for wherever you are going before you set off. Also, if all this travel information has fuelled your wanderlust, you can even book tickets and accommodation directly from the site.

Lonely Planet Online **www.lonelyplanet.co.uk**

If you're planning on backpacking around the world you'll probably already own at least one of the Lonely Planet series. Here you'll find a wealth of information from its travel guides and an advice forum written by travellers around the world.

Virtual Tourist **www.vtourist.com**

Virtual Tourist is definitely a strong contender for the title of the web's most established travel guide, having been around since 1994. Over the years the site has grown from being a simple world guide to something of a travel monster, with over 31,000 destinations covered in amazing detail.

World Travel Guide **www.wtgonline.com**

Not quite up to the standard of Lonely Planet or Rough Guides, but if you're looking for a brief, well-written guide to the world's cities and countries you'll find it (and more) here.

Book Tailor **www.booktailor.co.uk**

Customisable travel guide books at the touch of a button sounds great, and it is. Simply tell it where you're going and what you need to know and Book Tailor will deliver the personalised book directly to your door. Superb. If you want to buy a more traditional type of travel book you'll definitely want to check out Stanfords (**www.stanfords.co.uk**).

National Geographic **www.nationalgeographic.com**

Maps, forums, interactive features and, of course, plenty of award-winning photography make this site worth visiting even if you have no intention of travelling outside Cheltenham.

The Hitchhiker's Guide to the Galaxy **www.h2g2.com**

There can't be many sites which can claim to be a travel guide for the entire galaxy but, then again, there aren't many authors who could be compared to the late Douglas Adams. The Hitchhiker's Guide is like a tourist information site for alien visitors and attempts to explain everything there is to know about earth and beyond

– from the sensible ('All about Brussels, Belgium') to the bizarre ('Train Station Psychosis').

■ *The best of the rest*

The Discovery Channel **www.discoverychannel.com**
Travelling? Do it like they do on the Discovery Channel.

Wish You Were Here…? **www.wishyouwerehere.com**
Judith Chalmers and her happy band of celebrity holiday chums welcome you to their (very tanned) world.

Country guides

■ *The best of the best*

At UK **www.atuk.co.uk**
If your travel ambitions only stretch as far as the UK then this is most definitely the

site for you. Every county is featured with details of accommodation, tourist attractions and even a range of live webcams, so you can see where you're going before you get there. Splendid.

The rest of the best

Africa Guide **www.africaguide.com**

Africa Guide provides a wealth of advice for visitors and is also used as a means to attract foreign aid and charity donations. An easy-to-navigate front page makes it a simple matter to find the information you need and, if you're planning to visit, it'll tell you all you need to know.

Greenland **www.greenland-guide.dk**

It may be one of the coldest places on the planet, but Greenland has produced a surprisingly hot website to promote its wildlife and, erm, ice. For the adventurous there's plenty of information about dog sledding and whale watching, while animal lovers will be captivated by the pictures of furry creatures.

The best of the rest

Australia	**www.australia.com**
Austria	**www.austria-tourism.at**
Belgium	**www.visitbelgium.com**
Brazil	**www.brazilinfo.com/index_en.htm**
Caribbean	**www.caribtourism.com**
Denmark	**www.visitdenmark.com**
Egypt	**www.touregypt.net**
France	**www.francetourism.com**
Germany	**www.deutschland-tourismus.de/e/**
Greece	**www.travel-greece.com**
Ireland	**www.ireland.travel.ie**
Italy	**www.italiantourism.com**
Japan	**www.jnto.go.jp**
Mexico	**www.mexicanwave.com**
Netherlands	**www.holland.com**
Portugal	**www.portugal.org**
Russia	**www.russia-travel.com**
Switzerland	**www.switzerlandtourism.ch**
USA	**www.usatourist.com**

Place guides

■ *The best of the best*

Time Out **www.timeout.com**

London's Living Guide goes global, with a wide range of fresh and funky guides to the world's cities. If you're planning a family holiday with the kids then this may not be the site for you. If, however, you want to party in Prague or chill out in Chicago, there really is only one choice.

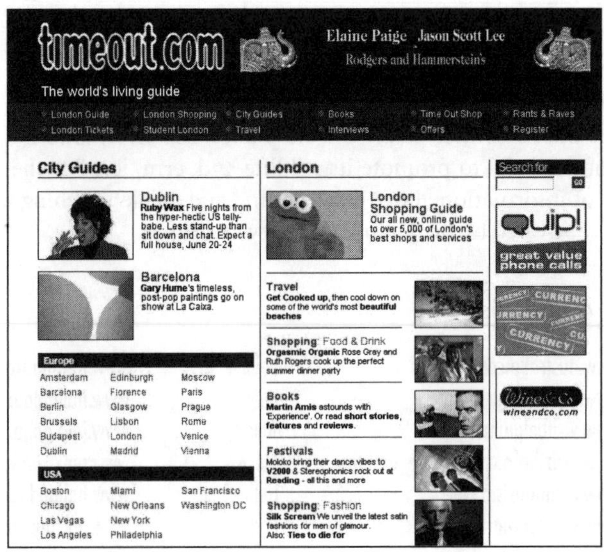

■ *The rest of the best*

Paris **www.paris.org**

Whether you're planning a visit to the Eiffel Tower and want to know what time it opens or you just want to find out more about the romance capital of Europe, you'll find all the answers within easy reach.

New York **www.nyctourist.com**

New York – home of the Empire State Building, the Statue of Liberty, yellow cabs, *Ghostbusters II* … the list goes on and on. The official site of the city that never sleeps contains plenty of information about what to see, where to go and, perhaps most importantly, how to stay safe. If you want to have a proper look around New York before you decide whether to make the trip, why not take a virtual tour with Strolling (**www.strolling.com**).

Thorpe Park **www.thorpepark.co.uk**

The home of the Tidal Wave doesn't disappoint with a virtual guide to the park, information about the latest rides and even online ticket booking to plan your visit in advance. White-knuckle fans should also check out Chessington World of Adventures (**www.chessington.co.uk**) and Alton Towers (**www.alton-towers.com**).

■ *The best of the rest*

Amsterdam	**www.channels.nl**	Great Barrier Reef	**www.great-barrier-reef.com**
Disneyland (Paris)	**www.disneylandparis.com**	London	**www.londontown.com**
Disneyworld (Florida)	**www.disneyworld.com**	Niagara Falls	**www.niagara-usa.com**
Edinburgh	**www.edinburghguide.com**	The Solar System	**www.nasa.gov**

Maps

■ *The best of the best*

Multimap **www.multimap.com**

No matter how good your sense of direction is, it helps to have a decent map. Multimap is much more than decent, as it allows you to enter any UK postcode or street name and instantly see a detailed map of the area. It's tools like this that make the internet worthwhile.

■ *The rest of the best*

MapQuest **www.mapquest.com**

MapQuest can be summed up in one word – huge. The main feature of the site is its map database, which will display a street map for pretty much any area in the world.

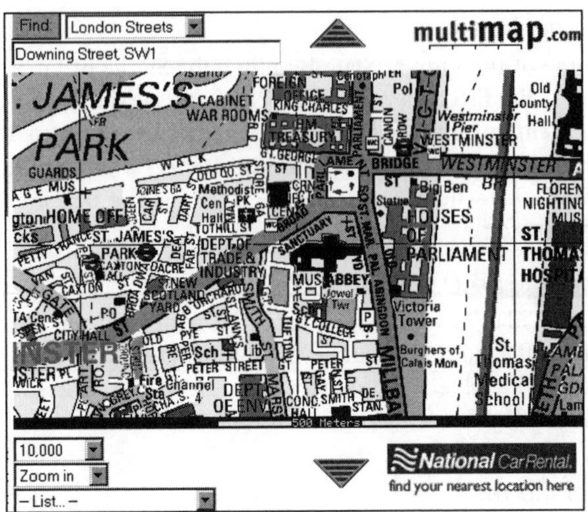

Expedia Maps **www.expedia.co.uk/daily/resources**

If MapQuest doesn't fit the bill, Expedia also allows you to search for maps for any major city or area in the world. The level of detail is not quite as good as Multimap, but when you've got this level of coverage it's difficult to complain.

Maps.com **www.maps.com**

If quality and detail are important to you, you'll probably need to spend some money on a proper map rather than using a service like Multimap or MapQuest. Maps.com allows you to buy maps in either downloadable digital format or on paper.

Atlapedia **www.atlapedia.com**

Offering an array of colourful maps backed up with geographic, economic and cultural information, Atlapedia is a must for globetrotters and geography students.

Terraserver **www.terraserver.com**

Not strictly a map site but well worth a look – if only for the novelty value. Features aerial photos of places of varying importance around the world, including major tourist attractions and airports. Hours of fun for Russian spies and lazy plane spotters.

Travel advice

■ *The best of the best*

About Travel **home.about.com/travel**

About.com uses real people to suggest appropriate links to appropriate information on everything from travel vaccines to treasure hunting. If you can't find the right section, try searching from the main menu page at **www.about.com.**

■ *The rest of the best*

Tips 4 Trips **www.tips4trips.com**

A forum for travellers to exchange tips and advice. The quality of the advice varies wildly, a particular favourite being 'Make sure you won't be vacationing in land mines ... on toxic beaches', but overall the contributors seem to know what they are talking about.

Epicurious Travel **travel.epicurious.com**

From the publishers of *Traveler* magazine, Epicurious Travel offers the usual mix of travel information and tips. The best part has got to be its world events guide, which will make sure that you never miss the party.

Outside Online **www.outsidemag.com**

Fans of the great outdoors will love this award-winning magazine dedicated to adventure and adventurers. Tales of courage and endurance are mixed with advice and discussion, making this an enjoyable destination for the more active traveller.

The Backpackers Guide **www.backpackers.net**

Written in a friendly style by people who have clearly been out there and done it, this site provides all you need to begin your Littlest Hobo-esque adventure.

The Complete Gap Year **www.gapyear.co.uk**

So you've finished your exams and the choice is whether to spend your gap year seeing the world or stocking shelves in Tesco. If you want to take the former route then a trip to The Complete Gap Year is absolutely essential – otherwise it's off to **www.tesco.com**.

Excite Travel **www.excite.com/travel**

If Excite Travel wasn't so American you probably wouldn't need too many other travel sites. Essentially just a handy directory of travel-related sites, you'll find links to everything from American Express to the Weather Channel.

Art of Travel **www.artoftravel.com**

Intelligent advice for travellers on a budget – clearly written by someone who's travelled the world and learnt the hard way.

Travel health and law

■ *The best of the best*

Centre for Disease Control and Prevention **www.cdc.gov/travel**

User-friendly health advice for British travellers, providing warnings about health risk areas, disease prevention advice and links to other useful resources.

The rest of the best

Foreign and Commonwealth Office **www.fco.gov.uk**

Avoid getting caught up in a military coup or malaria epidemic by consulting the government's Foreign and Commonwealth Office before you travel.

Embassy Web **www.embpage.org**

This complete list of embassies covers almost every nationality in almost every country and will prove invaluable if you find yourself in trouble abroad. Unfortunately the site doesn't include the dates of the ambassadors' receptions so you'll have to buy your own Ferrero Rocher. Eccellente.

Travel Health **www.travelhealth.com**

A very useful site which claims to be the premier health resource for travellers. Whilst there are a few other health sites which would argue with this claim, you would be hard pushed to find broader coverage of health and safety risks for people on the move.

Travel Safety Tips **www.travelsafetytips.com**
Concise yet potentially life-saving advice for travellers. If it doesn't make you more careful it'll certainly make you paranoid.

UK Passport Agency **www.ukpa.gov.uk**
Of course you'll have no need for this site as you've checked that your passport is valid, right? If for any reason you need to get hold of a passport application kit in a hurry or would just like to find out how to take the perfect passport photo (we kid you not), the answers are here.

Language

■ *The best of the best*

Travlang **www.travlang.com**
This no-frills site is a great first stop for learning the basics of a foreign language. Once you've chosen where you're travelling to, you are presented with a list of useful

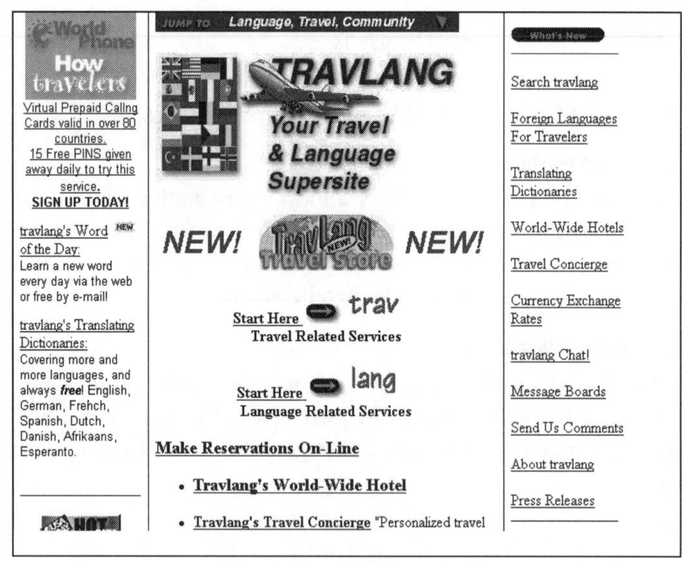

phrases which may not make you fluent but will certainly allow you to get by without resorting to mime.

The rest of the best

Fodors Language **www.fodors.com/language**

One of the best sites for learning basic conversational French, German, Italian or Spanish. Fodors is already renowned for its excellent travel guide site, and this invaluable resource is the icing on the cake.

Babel Fish **world.altavista.com**

Fans of the *Hitchhiker's Guide to the Galaxy* will recognise the Babel fish as a translating fish which 'caused more and bloodier wars than anything else in the history of creation'. On the internet, however, Babel Fish is actually a very nifty translation tool from AltaVista. Translations from Japanese can be a bit on the literal side – but without this amazing tool we'd never have heard that *The Cheese Went out to Somewhere?* had made it into Amazon's bestseller list (**www.amazon.co.jp**). As an added bonus, why not try converting English to French and then back again for an amusing one-player game of Chinese whispers. Literally minutes of fun.

Linguaphone **www.linguaphone.co.uk**

If you want to go the whole hog and learn a language properly then you'll need a proper in-depth course – and who better to provide it than Linguaphone? You'll have to shell out some pretty serious cash to start learning, but it's money well spent if you travel regularly.

Time

Now, thanks to the power of the internet, you can make your jetlag even worse by comparing local time with the time back home. Great.

The best of the best

Time and Date **www.timeanddate.com/worldclock**

Find out what time it is anywhere in the world – all on one page. One of those tools which doesn't look like much but that you'll visit time and time again. Great stuff.

Addis Ababa	17:18	Geneva *	16:18	New Orleans *	09:18
Adelaide	23:48	Guatemala	08:18	New York *	10:18
Aden	17:18	Halifax *	11:18	Oslo *	16:18
Aklavik *	08:18	Hanoi	21:18	Ottawa *	10:18
Algiers	15:18	Harare	16:18	Paris *	16:18
Amman *	17:18	Havana *	10:18	Perth	22:18
Amsterdam *	16:18	Helsinki *	17:18	Phoenix	07:18
Anadyr *	03:18+	Hong Kong	22:18	Prague *	16:18
Anchorage *	06:18	Honolulu	04:18	Rangoon	20:48
Ankara *	17:18	Houston *	09:18	Reykjavik	14:18
Antananarivo	17:18	Indianapolis	09:18	Rio de Janeiro	11:18
Asuncion	10:18	Islamabad	19:18	Riyadh	17:18

The rest of the best

World Time Zone **www.worldtimezone.com**

A bit more complicated than Time and Date, with world time zones displayed on a colourful map which somehow manages to make it seem much more confusing. Great for geography students, but a bit too much like hard work for the rest of us.

relationships and marriage 9

Before you can start a family, it's pretty important to find someone special to start it with. In this chapter we concentrate on those early pre-family days – from dating and relating through to actually tying the knot. As with so much else, the internet makes it simple.

Dating

■ *The best of the best*

Cosmic Cupid **www.cosmiccupid.com**

Too shy to flirt face-to-face? Want to test the water before diving in with both feet? Let Cosmic Cupid make the first move for you via e-mail or text message. It's all completely anonymous and, who knows, you might even get lucky. GSOH essential.

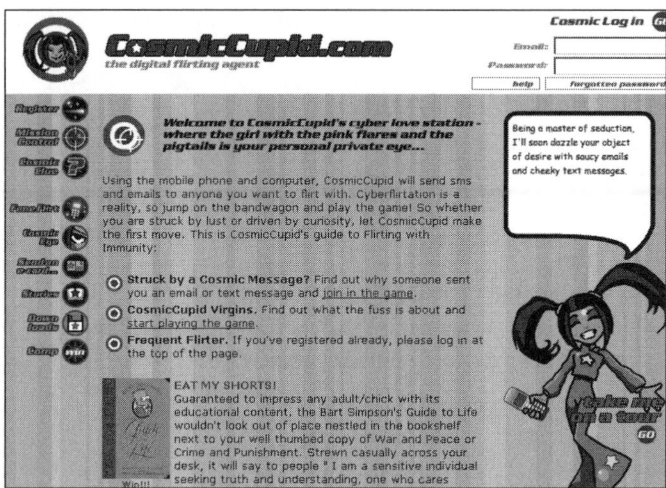

The rest of the best

Dateline **www.dateline.uk.com**

As the world's largest, most successful and longest-established introduction agency, you'd expect something pretty special from Dateline. In reality, its site actually looks a little amateurish, with lots of text but a distinct lack of style – it's not obvious whether you're supposed to join before you search the database or search then join. Having said that, appearances aren't everything and the service has a huge number of users and an impressive track record for matching suitable people.

About Dating **dating.about.com**

As the name suggests, About Dating concentrates on the best online resources for finding someone special, with hundreds of links, some well-written articles and even discussion forums.

Personals 365 **www.personals365.com**

The 365 Corporation continues its quest for online domination with this fresh and funky dating site for the internet generation. Traditionalists will be pleased to hear that the clichéd pictures of happy, smiling romantics are still here, but the rest of the service is bang up to date with instant registration, real-time chat (no more premium-rate phone calls!) and everything else you need to start meeting new and exciting people. For an equally modern but thoroughly American alternative, try Match (**www.match.com**).

Lifestyle.UK Dating **www.lifestyle.co.uk/eh.htm**

A frighteningly complete list of links to UK dating sites, offering everything from dating for music lovers to Russian brides and even professional alibi services. If you can't find a partner from one of these then perhaps online dating isn't for you.

Wild 5 **www.wild5.com**

Describing itself as 'kind of like taking an 18-30 holiday', Wild 5 definitely knows its audience. Sign up, create a profile, meet, chat and even arrange a virtual date – because staying in is the new going out. Apparently.

■ *The best of the rest*

Dating Direct **www.datingdirect.com**
Slick, purple and packed to the rafters with dateless hopefuls.

Webpersonals **www.webpersonals.com**
Tens of thousands of potential partners, all looking for ... erm ... company.

Marriage and weddings

■ *The best of the best*

Confetti **www.confetti.co.uk**
This complete wedding portal offers pretty much everything you could possibly need to organise your big day – advice and ideas, dresses, venues, speeches, stag and hen nights, planning tools, reception planning, gift lists, suppliers and even message boards to swap advice with friends, families and fiancés nation-wide. Excellent.

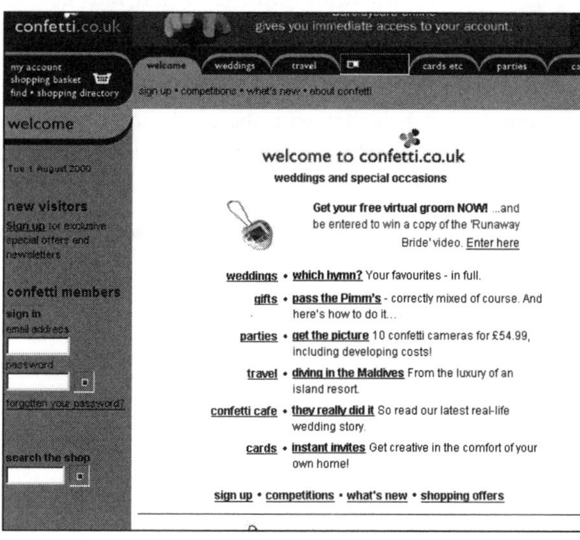

The rest of the best

Wedding Guide **www.weddingguide.co.uk**

On first appearances, Wedding Guide looks a bit like the online equivalent of those glossy wedding magazines you see in newsagents – supermodel bride on the cover, screaming headlines offering information and advice, relationship tests to see if it's all a big mistake – you know the drill. Once you get past the front page, however, you'll find a wealth of information for both the bride and groom, including advice, services, forums, chat and shopping, all presented in an easy-to-browse format.

Wedding Day **www.wedding-day.co.uk**

From hiring a marquee to choosing the right bridal underwear, all the answers are here – and although there are fewer frills than on some of the other sites, if it's useful and reliable information you're after, you won't find better. For more of the same, with even fewer frills, check out Hitched (**www.hitched.co.uk**).

Web Wedding **www.webwedding.co.uk**

A slightly more cluttered approach to the wedding portal business, Web Wedding offers a similar range of features to Confetti but with a more noticeably commercial angle. Shopping aside, the information on offer is first-rate, covering everything from choosing the right music to organising the honeymoon.

Wedding Circle **www.weddingcircle.com**

The great thing about weddings is that, with the exception of a few quirky customs, the advice is the same no matter where you live. With this in mind, this thoroughly American site is well worth a look if you need some tips on arranging photographers, food, speeches, invitations and flowers.

parenting 10

Pregnancy and childbirth

If you need some advice before your little bundle of joy arrives on the scene, look no further than these excellent pregnancy sites. For more general health advice, flip straight to the next chapter, on Health.

The best of the best

The Baby Registry www.thebabyregistry.co.uk

From common pregnancy health issues and complaints to getting contraception advice, via chat and shopping, it's all here – and the blokes haven't been forgotten either, with their very own 'for dads' section. Nice.

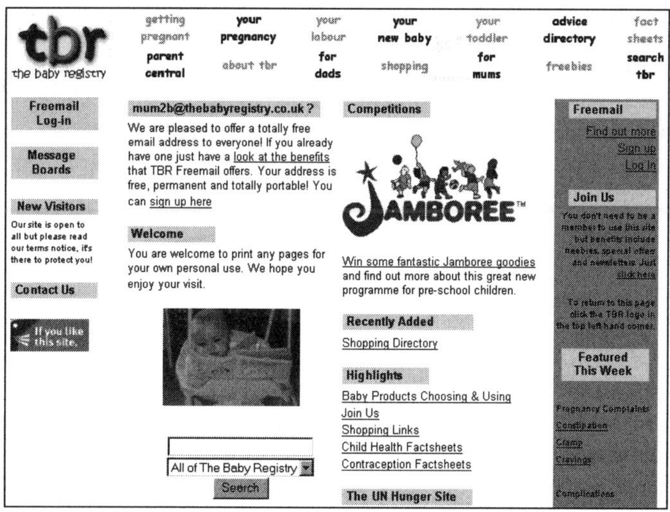

■ *The rest of the best*

Precious Little One **www.preciouslittleone.com**

A useful guide to pregnancy-related matters including health, childcare, shopping and even choosing the right name for your little one. Also includes a baby gallery with an 'aaaaah' factor of 10.

Pregnancy Calendar **www.pregnancycalendar.com**

The Pregnancy Calendar is one of those ideas which could only really work properly on the internet. You type in either the conception or due date of your baby and the site builds a day-by-day, fully customised, calendar detailing the development of your little 'un to give you an idea of what to expect and when.

FPA **www.fpa.org.uk**

This excellent site from FPA (formerly the Family Planning Association) presents a very good case for freedom of choice, with plenty of help and advice and details of its latest campaigns. For more of the same, check out the British Pregnancy and Advisory Service (**www.bpas.org**) while, if you believe that the prevention is better than the cure, you might want to take a quick visit to Condomania (**www.condomania.co.uk**).

National Childbirth Trust **www.nct-online.org**

The sheer number of expertly written articles on subjects as diverse as alcohol during pregnancy and coping with colic, combined with photos of newborns with little scrunched up faces, makes this an essential bookmark for anyone considering, expecting or looking after a baby. By the way the picture of the smiling male model with the rather confused-looking child wins our 'blatant attempt at gender equality' award. Congratulations to everyone involved.

Childcare

■ *The best of the best*

Urbia **www.urbia.co.uk**

From common questions about baby food and nappies to thorny issues like drug abuse and under-age sex, the site is with you every step of the way. The content is

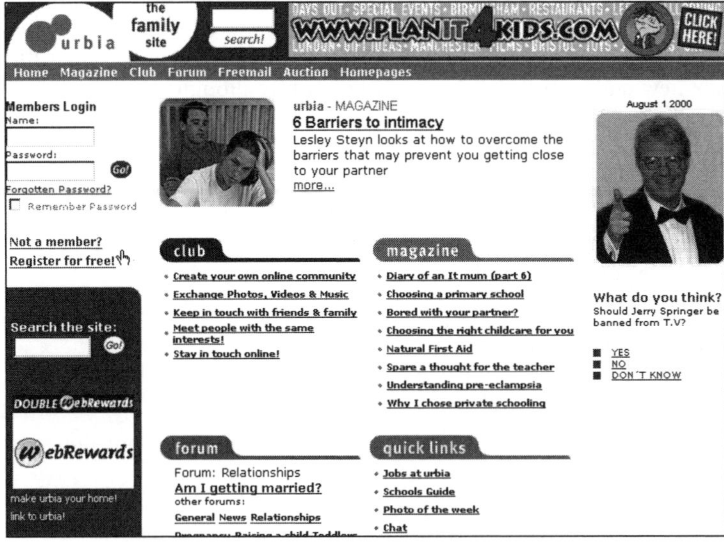

excellent and the layout is absolutely faultless. For complete 0–18 coverage, nothing else comes close.

The rest of the best

UK Parents **www.ukparents.co.uk**

UK Parents is an absolutely invaluable resource for new mums and dads, with birth stories, diaries, photos, forums, competitions, advice, recipes and even a parent shop where you can stock up on all those kiddie essentials. Like an electronic coffee morning. Without the biscuits. For more of the same, check out Parents Online (**www.parents.org.uk**).

E-Mum **www.e-mum.com**

Dads? Who are they? This one is purely for the mums, preferably those who are also trying to hold down a job while raising a youngster. The website for the UK's working mums is a slick source of information on a whole range of relevant issues, including health, childcare, finding a childminder, finding a job and even choosing the right educational books.

Huggies Club **www.huggiesclub.com**

This Huggies-sponsored site features a wealth of well-put-together features and advice for new and expecting mums – once you've ploughed through the lengthy registration process.

Baby World **www.babyworld.co.uk**

Over 2,500 pages of wonderfully cluttered but beautifully written baby information on all of the usual subjects, plus an extremely well-stocked shop full of all the toys, games and accessories your little one could ever want.

The best of the rest

Missing Kids **www.missingkids.co.uk**

Help track down missing children and nail the abductors. Excellent site.

My Family **www.myfamily.com**

Create a personal homepage for your family. Free and easy to use.

The web has some excellent health resources both in terms of actual medical advice and support for those who are suffering from a particular illness or disease, but it's important to tread carefully. Unless you know who's behind a particular site it's probably not a good idea to believe everything you read, as anyone can put up a medical website – no recognised qualifications are required. The best advice is to always consult your doctor before acting on any information off the web.

Health portals

■ *The best of the best*

Net Doctor www.netdoctor.co.uk

Arguably the best health site on the internet, Net Doctor contains more information

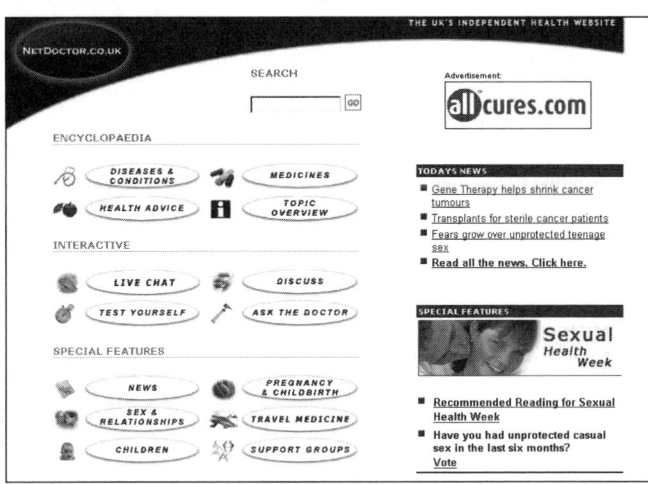

than you can shake a thermometer at, including an A to Z of diseases, advice on medicines, self tests, health news, discussion and support groups, and even an Ask the Doctor feature where a team of expert doctors, including TV's Dr Hilary Jones, will attempt to answer your medical questions. Completely indispensable.

■ *The best of the rest*

BBC Health **www.bbc.co.uk/health**

Regardless of your ailment, you'll find information, support, advice and plenty of links to other online medical resources here. As with the other BBC sites there are plenty of programme tie-ins, so expect to see the cast of *EastEnders* lecturing you about the importance of exercise, and plenty of references to Holby City Hospital.

Health in Focus **www.healthinfocus.co.uk**

Health in Focus claims to offer 'information, knowledge and choice' to UK patients, health workers and carers, and it broadly achieves this. In addition to the searchable database of health information, there are advice guides, news summaries and plenty of other features to have you back on your feet in no time.

NHS Direct **www.nhsdirect.nhs.uk**

Excellent health resource designed to cut waiting times. Basically, the site's main role is to determine whether your symptoms are serious enough to warrant a trip to casualty, a ride in an ambulance or whether that stomach pain is just a side-effect of last night's curry. Hypochondriacs will have a field day – while the rest of us will probably want a second opinion.

Surgery Door **www.surgerydoor.co.uk**

Dr Mark Porter's guide to family health and fitness is suitably well informed and considerably less smarmy than the good doctor himself.

■ *The best of the rest*

Dr Koop **www.drkoop.net**

Excellent American medical advice site – but would you trust someone called Dr Koop? Didn't think so.

Health Gate UK **www.healthgate.co.uk**

Not exactly the most comprehensive or friendly medical site, but well worth visiting for a second opinion.

Specific advice

The best of the best

First Aid **members.tripod.co.uk/rescue**

This site may be an amateur effort but it's difficult to fault the quality of advice on offer. A positive cornucopia of first aid information is provided, from minor cuts and grazes to dealing with phobias and panic attacks. Excellent.

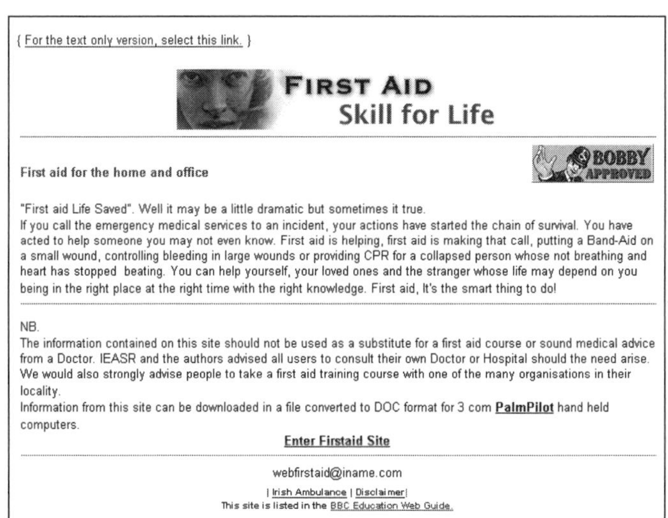

The rest of the best

British Heart Foundation **www.bhf.org.uk**

This excellent resource from the British Heart Foundation provides loads of useful information to help you take care of your heart, including publications, advice and a very useful A to Z of cardiac-related terms. Remember how important it is to look after your heart – you only get one. Unless of course you're Doctor Who.

The Samaritans **www.samaritans.org**

The Samaritans have made good use of the web to promote the services they offer, as well as providing information about your local branch and useful advice for coping with stress. An impressive site for a life-saving service. For alcohol worries, check out Alcoholics Anonymous (**www.alcoholics-anonymous.org.uk**).

Pfizer **www.pfizer.com**

Slick medical advice and information from the people who brought us Viagra. Nice site guys, keep it up.

Achoo **www.achoo.com**

Have we missed something? Don't panic, whatever medical information you need, there's almost certainly a link to it here.

■ *The best of the rest*

Diabetic Association	**www.diabetes.org.uk**
Imperial Cancer Research Fund	**www.icnet.uk**
Internet Mental Health	**www.mentalhealth.com**
Meningitis Research Foundation	**www.meningitis.org.uk**
Royal National Institute for the Blind	**www.rnib.org.uk**

Health and beauty shopping

■ *The best of the best*

All Cures **www.allcures.com**

All Cures is the UK's first full-service online pharmacy and it's genuinely very impressive. The site is stocked with everything you'd expect to find in your local branch of Boots, including over-the-counter medicines, beauty products, toiletries, alternative medicines, photographic services and even NHS and private prescriptions. Love it.

The rest of the best

Think Natural **www.thinknatural.com**

If you're looking for natural health products, Think Natural should definitely be your first port of call. Combining a well-stocked shop and a wealth of useful health advice, keeping the doctor away has never been easier.

Boots **www.boots.co.uk**

A combination of shop and magazine, with advice on health, beauty and parenting, plus the opportunity to stock up on everything you need to make you look (and smell) better – you can even collect Advantage Card points if you're into that sort of thing.

Look Fantastic **www.lookfantastic.com**

While Boots has taken the clutter-free, pastel-coloured design route, Look Fantastic is beautifully busy, with plenty of exclamation marks and unbelievable offers. The big cosmetic names are all here, including Wella, Paul Mitchell and Aveda – some at impressive discounts of up to 60 per cent – and the Which? Web Trader logo will make your shopping less stressful.

My Nutrition **www.mynutrition.co.uk**

Back to the pastel colours (hurray!) with this award-winning 'online guide for everything to do with healthy food, eating and supplements'. The shopping area is only a very small part of what's on offer here, with news, a free nutrition consultation and expert advice all thrown in for good measure.

The best of the rest

Avon **www.uk.avon.com**

The whole Avon range is available on this easy-to-use, if slightly bland, site. There are some pretty reasonable discounts for ordering online.

Iris Online **www.iris-online.co.uk**

Iris Online provides a simple but very effective way to buy contact lenses without paying over the odds for them. Simply send them your lens prescription and they'll supply everything you need. There's not really much else to say – the site is well laid out, shopping is easy and the prices are pretty good too. Sorted.

Condoms 4u **www.condoms4u.com**

No more embarrassment in the chemist with this well-designed and well-stocked store. There's a wide range to choose from, and all orders are dispatched in a plain wrapper to avoid knowing looks from the postman. Stop sniggering at the back.

Burgins Perfumery **www.burginsperfumery.co.uk**

The design may leave something to be desired, but you can't fault the range of perfumes stocked by this York-based site. The site is separated into products for him and products for her, all catalogued into alphabetical order – from Acqua di Giò to Zut.

The English Shaving Company **www.theenglishshavingcompany.co.uk**

Shaving need no longer be a chore with this impressive range of shaving accessories, shaving creams and aftershaves from some of the UK's most established names. The prices are far from cheap – but then again, what price shaving perfection?

Perfume Directory **www.perfumedirectory.co.uk**

Another no-frills fragrance site, this time complete with photographs so you know what you're buying.

education 12

Learning something new every day just got a whole lot easier thanks to the huge electronic library that is the internet. Pre-school, infant, primary, secondary, higher – it doesn't matter what level you're at, a quick browse through one of our recommended sites will have you on the road to educational enlightenment.

Education portals

■ *The best of the best*

BBC Education www.bbc.co.uk/education

From pre-school to higher education, you'll find something for everyone, including

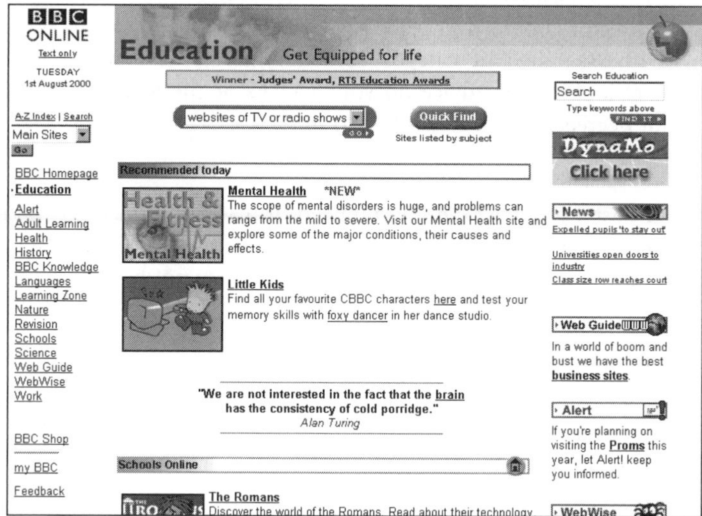

plenty of blatant programme tie-ins – all in the best possible taste of course – and there's a superb internet guide if you're still a little unsure about all this web malarkey.

The rest of the best

Learnfree **www.learnfree.co.uk**

This really is impressive. From pre-school to over-16s, Learnfree is one of the slickest education portals in the business, with news, features, advice, forums, polls, revision guides and even cookery tips – if you're a parent you'll wonder how you ever lived without it.

Schools Net **www.schoolsnet.com**

If you're trying to choose the right school, college or university for yourself or your kids, Schools Net could well be the answer to your prayers. Along with an in-depth guide to 22,202 UK schools (count 'em), there's news, book reviews, revision tools, discussion forums and so much more. For more of the same, with a European flavour, check out European Schools Net (**www.eun.org**).

Search Gate **www.searchgate.co.uk**

This massive directory boasts over 5,000 academic, student and careers resources, all of which can be searched by category or with the aid of a handy search box. Whether you're looking for advice on your GCSEs or the textbooks you need to complete your degree, this is a great place to start.

Top Marks **www.topmarks.co.uk**

If Search Gate hasn't provided the site you need, Top Marks is the place to look for a second opinion. Over 1,000 high-quality resources are listed along with descriptions, so you know exactly what to expect. It may not be the best education search tool, but it looks good and works well. Try it.

Education Unlimited **www.educationunlimited.co.uk**

There's a strong emphasis here on educational news as opposed to actually teaching you anything – but if you are a teacher, a student or a parent who likes to know what's going on behind the scenes, this excellent site should be one of your first ports of call.

The Times Educational Supplement **www.tes.co.uk**

No review of education sites would be complete without mentioning the *TES*. Not only can you read extracts from each week's issue completely free of charge, but this impressive site also offers constantly updated news bulletins and links to other *Times* websites.

The National Grid for Learning **www.ngfl.gov.uk**

Nothing to do with electricity, the National Grid for Learning is a government initiative designed to allow schools and pupils to share educational resources around the UK and even across the globe.

The best of the rest

Advisory Centre For Education **www.ace-ed.org.uk**

News and information specifically for parents, school governors and teachers.

Parentline Plus **www.parentlineplus.org.uk**

Ultra-slick charity site offering help and advice to parents and guardians, with online info and a free phone helpline.

Still not found the education resource you're looking for? If it's not listed in one of the age-group categories below, make sure you check out Eduweb (**www.eduweb.co.uk**), which is packed full of resources and links to the best of the educational web, surprisingly enough.

Pre-school and infants

The best of the best

Fun School **www.funschool.com**

The great thing about pre-school education sites is that the National Curriculum hasn't kicked in yet so, provided there's an educational element and a sense of fun, it's up to the parents to decide what the rules are. With that in mind, this American site is a great resource for both kids and parents, with fun, games and enough child-friendly links to keep the kids clicking until they get to primary school.

The rest of the best

Mamamedia www.mamamedia.com

If Fun School doesn't make the grade (sorry) then you'll definitely want to check out Mamamedia. It may be ridiculously bright and garish in design, but it's hard to fault the sheer number of games, toys and general educational activities the site contains.

Winnie the Pooh www.winniethepooh.co.uk

A.A. Milne's furry creation has long been an icon for kids around the world – a status which is destined to continue long after technology kills off other low-tech favourites if this excellent site is anything to go by.

Coloring www.coloring.com

Every child loves colouring – perhaps some enjoy colouring on the walls and the sofa more than they enjoy using colouring books but, nevertheless, it's all good fun! Long-suffering parents will be pleased to hear that help is at hand in the form of this excellent no-crayons colourathon.

Big Brainy Babies www.brainybabies.com

Got a particularly clued-up bundle of joy? This is the site for you. Brainy Babies contains a whole world of puzzles, trivia and games for young children, although the site's main purpose is to sell you an educational beanbag toy thing.

Primary school

■ *The best of the best*

Spark Island www.sparkisland.com

A superb English, maths and science learning resource for primary school children. Parents and teachers can register for a free one-month trial before deciding whether to subscribe. Well worth a look.

■ *The rest of the best*

Bonus www.bonus.com

If you're using Bonus purely as an educational resource rather than just a way of teaching computer literacy, then bear in mind that as it's based in the USA there may be some information which doesn't fit in with what's taught in UK schools. That aside, the site is great for younger kids and may even keep the adults occupied for a lunch break or two. Oh, and the background music will drive you up the wall. Enjoy.

Surf Monkey **www.surfmonkey.com**

More clunky, chunky design, this time from the bizarrely titled Surf Monkey. There are plenty of features, including a guide to cool sites, fun and games, competitions, discussion forums and even the Surf Monkey Club which offers e-mail, chat, bulletin boards and a birthday wish list.

Yucky **www.yucky.com**

Yucky takes a fun and interactive look at human bodily functions, including burping, farting, spots and nose picking and all those other things which adults disapprove of (in public anyway) and kids can't get enough of. The production values are top-notch and the information, while it may be a little ... erm … in your face, is as accurate as it is engaging. Snot and science? A guaranteed winner.

Homework Solver **www.homeworksolver.com**

Simply choose a year group, select your subject and you'll be provided with a whole world of advice on answering standard questions. The beauty of the site is that it doesn't answer the question for you – providing instead a gentle shove towards what the teacher is looking for.

Web 66 **web66.coled.umn.edu**

Web 66 lists sites designed by primary schools around the world in a slick, easy-to-browse format, allowing you to easily home in on your local centre of academic excellence to see what they have to offer.

Secondary school

■ *The best of the best*

BBC Bitesize GCSE **www.bbc.co.uk/education/revision**

BBC Bitesize claims to be the 'first ever revision guide via TV, books and the internet',

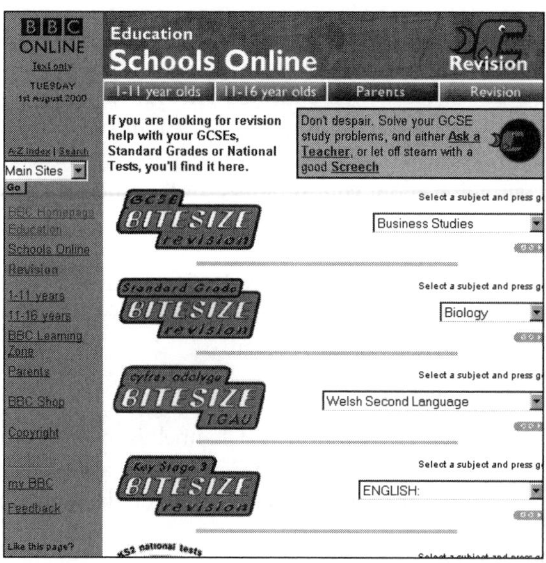

although the well-produced site is probably enough without having to resort to the other media, with nuggets of information and revision tips for pretty much every GCSE subject plus the option to e-mail a teacher if you need help on a particular question. It's free, it works and it looks pretty darn special too. Another winner.

The rest of the best

Revise It **www.reviseit.com**

Revise It aims to take some of the stress out of the GCSE process by providing revision tips, forums, features and a mutually helpful community of students who help each other make the most of their revision time.

A Levels **www.a-levels.co.uk**

Plenty of categorised links to the best sites and tools on the web to help you study for your A levels. For the same type of thing, but with the focus on GCSEs, check out Project GCSE (**www.projectgcse.co.uk**).

The Learning Shop **www.learningshop.com**

Despite the slightly naff name (sorry, but it is), this excellent site contains more features than you can shake a well-educated stick at, including revision guides, news, study tips and some nifty multimedia stuff. Parents and teachers needn't feel left out either, as the site also boasts a lounge which is almost certainly a hotbed of tea drinking and whinging about your progress (or lack thereof).

Maths Help **www.maths-help.co.uk**

The concept couldn't be simpler – if you're having trouble with a homework or revision question, you send it to the site and a maths expert will e-mail you with advice on how to go about solving the problem.

History Channel **www.historychannel.com**

Although the official site of the History Channel is not specifically aimed at students in secondary education, it provides so much easy-to-digest information that any GCSE or A-level history student will want to bookmark it immediately.

New Scientist **www.newscientist.com**

Up-to-the-minute scientific information, thought-provoking articles and some of the highest standards of presentation and writing on the web make this essential viewing – even if the limit of your scientific aspirations is using a Bunsen burner to set fire to your eyebrows. Love it.

Further and higher education

■ *The best of the best*

UCAS **www.ucas.ac.uk**

There's no two ways about it – if you're off to college or university, you shouldn't make any decisions until you've checked out this excellent resource from the Universities and Colleges Admissions Service. Our favourite feature is the exhaustive listing of every institution in the UK, complete with information on available courses, contact details and links to their official sites.

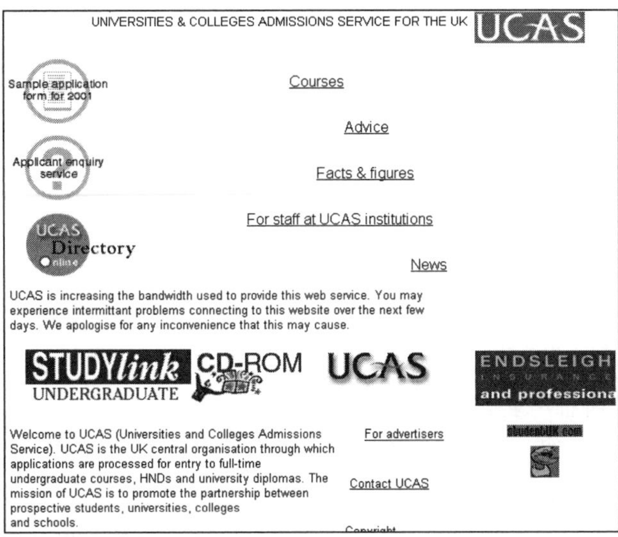

The rest of the best

The National Union of Students **www.nus.org.uk**

Your NUS card is more than just a passport to cheap beer and cinema tickets, apparently. The National Union of Students site is full of useful information on student rights and campaigns, advice on how much money you're entitled to – and how to get it – plus everything else you need to fully prepare yourself for higher education. Except perhaps a love of daytime television and cold pizza – but you'll soon pick that up.

Hobsons **www.hobsons.co.uk**

Essentially, Hobsons is an online guide to courses offered by popular UK universities, but there's also plenty of information on overseas learning and employment as well as some useful leisure guides to help you chill out. A great all-round resource.

Info Youth **www.infoyouth.com**

Billing itself as a complete guide to opportunities for young people in the UK, Info Youth certainly seems to offer almost everything you could need to get the best start in life. The site is part of the Schools Net network, so when it promises an in-depth guide to every university in Britain you know it *means* in-depth. Not only that, there are also career profiles, gap year opportunities, discussion forums and much more.

Edunet **www.edunet.com**

Extremely useful search tool, allowing you to find the best courses and institutions around the world. Enter your chosen subject and the country you want to study in and leave the rest to Edunet – simple really.

■ *The best of the rest*

Student Loans Company **www.slc.co.uk**

Everything you ever wanted to know about the SLC but were too skint to ask.

Unofficial Guides **www.unofficial-guides.com**

Don't choose a university until you find out what existing students think, using this extremely handy resource.

One of the (many) great things about the internet is that sites can cater for specific groups without having to worry about providing something for everyone. In recent years a number of sites have sprung up which are aimed specifically at men, women, children, teenagers, students, senior citizens and almost every other group of people you can think of.

Sites for men

■ *The best of the best*

mens-care.org **www.mens-care.org**

We like this one a lot. Like an electronic men's health handbook, mens-care.org provides in-depth advice on a wide range of issues, from prostate problems and

cancer to blood pressure problems and healthy eating. Once you've been worried half to death by all the talk of possible illnesses and diseases, you can even complete an instant assessment to either calm your fears or compound them. Very well put together and a potential life-saver.

■ *The rest of the best*

FHM **www.fhm.com**

All of the production values and quality articles you'd expect in the paper edition but free of charge and with added interaction. Women, sport, jokes, women, features, film and music reviews, women, editorial, competitions and women. Something for everyone, then.

Uploaded **www.uploaded.com**

A regularly updated front-page rant, live webcam, celebrity interviews, competitions and all the stuff you'd expect to find in the online edition of *Loaded* magazine make for a great way to spend a lunch break. Needs a good tidy-up though.

Men's Health **www.menshealth.co.uk**

Men's Health is yet another online version of a popular magazine, but this time the content is a little less focused on the opposite sex. There's a selection of features from the magazine covering health, fitness and sex plus an archive of previous editions, but the main purpose of the site seems to be to sell you a subscription. For more of the same, check out GQ (**www.swoon.com/mag_rack/gq.html**).

Lycos Men's Health **www.lycos.co.uk/webguides/health/m_men.html**

Directory site Lycos brings together a wide range of men's health and lifestyle sites in this impressive mini web guide. From aerobics to Viagra, via fitness and fun, you'll find it all here.

The best of the rest

Guy Rules www.guyrules.com

Undo millions of years of evolution with this handy guide to being a guy. Sense of humour essential.

Maxim www.maxim-magazine.co.uk

You know the drill by now – women, jokes, football and competitions.

Sites for women

The best of the best

Handbag www.handbag.com

Whereas some of the other 'women's portals' prefer to use flash graphics and pictures of beautiful people rather than any proper substance to attract users, Handbag has got the balance just about right, with well-written features on careers,

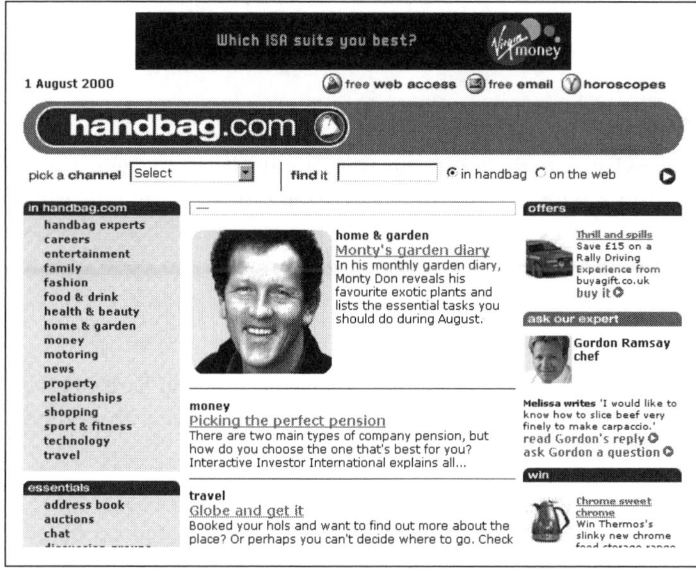

entertainment, fashion, food and drink, health and beauty, home and garden, money, motoring, news, property, relationships, shopping, sport and fitness, technology, travel and more. Superb.

The rest of the best

iCircle **www.icircle.co.uk**

Freeserve's women's channel is packed full of everything you'd expect to find in a traditional women's mag plus loads of interactivity, online shopping, chat, discussions and, of course, access to the whole network of Freeserve sites.

The Women's Institute **www.womens-institute.org.uk**

The online WI offers news, advice and so much more – with an easy-to-use interface that makes browsing a joy. Superb.

Women.com **www.women.com**

Women.com is based in America and was one of the first sites to concentrate solely on female issues. The range of content is a bit more far-reaching than the UK sites, with channels for entertainment, the internet and politics – although American politics is probably not that high on your list of interests.

BEME **www.beme.com**

The 'first place for women on the web' certainly looks impressive, with beautiful people plastered all over the front page (the cast of *Ally McBeal* when we last looked in) and an ultra-hip (and ultra-slow) navigation system. Speed criticisms aside, the content is impressive enough, with news, entertainment, horoscopes, discussion forums and competitions – and if you have fast internet access at work you'll have hours of fun.

Charlotte Street **www.charlottestreet.co.uk**

Like BEME, Charlotte Street is another site which tries too hard to be cool at the expense of speed and ease of navigation – but, like BEME, it's also packed with decent content.

PS Magazine **www.psmagazine.co.uk**

PS exists both as a normal glossy magazine and as this equally glossy website. The depth of content may not compare with Handbag and iCircle but if you're looking for shopping and fashion, it's a thoroughly enjoyable read.

■ *The best of the rest*

Ampnet **www.ampnet.co.uk**
Impressive looking online magazine for women with attitude. Excellent articles which might even appeal to men too.

PlanetGrrl **www.planetgrrl.com**
Sharp and sassy online magazine focusing on a wide range of grrl-related issues. Includes the straight-talking Dear PlanetGrrl where 'angst-ridden gals can come for honest straightforward grrl advice'.

Precious Online **www.preciousonline.co.uk**
Great looking UK-based site designed exclusively for black women. It may not have tons of content (yet), but the quality of writing makes it well worth a look.

Vogue **www.vogue.co.uk**
Looking for fashion news and plenty of photos? Strike a pose.

Sites for kids

■ *The best of the best*

Children's BBC **www.bbc.co.uk/cbbc**
All the favourites are here, including *Newsround* and *Blue Peter*, and just about every other CBBC programme – each with its own feature-packed website complete with news, competitions, games, presented profiles and behind-the-scenes gossip.

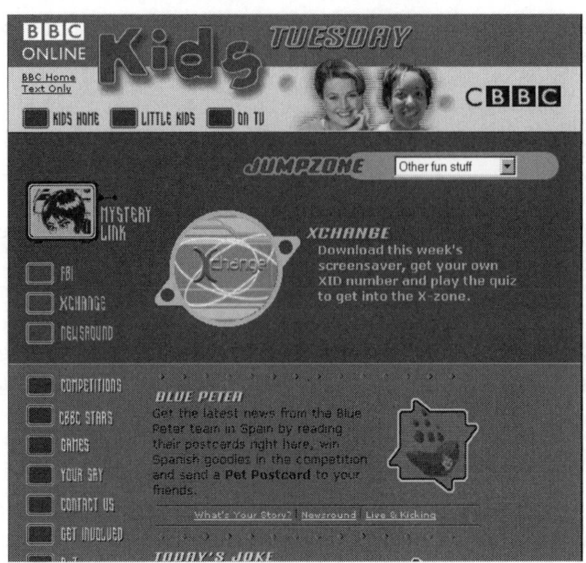

The rest of the best

Children's ITV **www.citv.co.uk**

Competing with the BBC for both viewers and site visitors, Children's ITV has put together an impressive site offering programme information, free e-mail, discussion forums and links to the best of the web.

Kid's Space **www.kids-space.org**

Stories, music, penpals, art galleries, county information and loads of interactive features, all in a child-friendly atmosphere which will keep the youngsters clicking away for hours.

KidsCom **www.kidscom.com**

For children who have outgrown Kid's Space, KidsCom provides equally engaging content but targeted at a slightly older age group. Penpals and chat, games and fun, polls and forums, links and even the chance to e-mail a world leader about young people's issues. For more of the same, with a British accent, check out Kids Channel (**www.kids-channel.co.uk**).

Sites for teenagers

■ *The best of the best*

The Site **www.thesite.org.uk**

Managing the seemingly impossible task of providing advice and information to young people without patronising or moralising, The Site is an essential visit for anyone concerned about sex, drugs, alcohol, health, money, education and the rest.

■ *The rest of the best*

Phat Start **www.phatstart.com**

Phat Start is quite possibly America's finest teenage portal, one of the 'by teens for teens' set. Celebrity info, pop culture, sport, homework, gaming, music, fashion, jokes, horoscopes, penpals and even religion are covered in impressive detail, with a network of other Phat sites just a mouse click away. The content on Phat Start is suitable for all, but if you want a female-only version, check out Nothing Pink (**www.nothingpink.com**).

Riot Grrl **www.riotgrrl.com**

Smart and sassy features, girl power fashion tips and an unhealthy obsession with Keanu Reeves make this well worth a look for independently minded young women. Zig-ah-zig-ahh.

Refresh **www.refreshmagazine.com**

A no-frills but strangely compelling combination of entertainment news, reviews and lively discussion. It's all a bit green, but well worth a look.

The best of the rest

Monster Teenzone **teenzone.monster.co.uk**

Get the best start for your career from one of the internet's most impressive employment sites.

Teen Chat **www.teenchat.co.uk**

Chat to teenagers across the UK. It's always busy and it's completely free.

Sites for students

The best of the best

Student World **www.student-world.co.uk**

Student World is an extremely funky-looking site offering all of the usual features (news, advice and articles) plus a decent amount of 'serious' information about choosing a course, planning your career and generally sorting out your life. For a mixture of fun and function, you won't do much better than this.

The rest of the best

Student.co.uk **www.student.co.uk**

You'd expect a site which had the foresight to register the name **Student.co.uk** name before anyone else to be something pretty special. Fortunately **Student.co.uk** dosen't disappoint with its nicely balanced blend of uni-related information and entertainment. The handy guides to stuudent life are worth the price of admission alone.

Student UK **www.studentuk.com**

The shades-wearing duck tells you straight away that Student UK is concerned with the lighter side of higher education. Yes, there's job information and yes, there's some excellent advice – but what we like best are the fun bits which include games, competitions, sports news, film and music reviews and shopping. Another great excuse to skip lectures.

Big Blue Spot **www.bigbluespot.com**

A nice range of information and features, but the really exciting thing about Big Blue Spot is that it's giving away free computers to students. Yes, free.

Red Mole **www.redmole.co.uk**

The emphasis here is on creating a community of students with forums, a nonsense exchange (don't ask), polls and even a problem page. It may not be the best-looking site in its field, but that won't stop you spending hours and hours using it.

Hot Toast **www.hot-toast.co.uk**

The main aim of this service is to provide free internet access, and with its rather nifty online sign-up feature you don't even need a CD. But if you don't fancy changing your internet service provider there's loads of other stuff to do on the site, including a decent selection of lifestyle articles, celebrity interviews, competitions and links to other studenty sites.

Sites for seniors

■ *The best of the best*

Vavo.com **www.vavo.com**

Combining seriously useful features with a certain sense of fun makes Vavo a winner in our book (quite literally). News, education, finance, health and fitness, history, leisure, politics, shopping, travel and work are among the subjects explored on the site, but the real selling point is the huge amount of interactivity on offer. You can use the reunions section to track down long-lost friends and family, place an advert in the classifieds section or just set the world to rights in the chat rooms and forums. As refreshing as it is impressive.

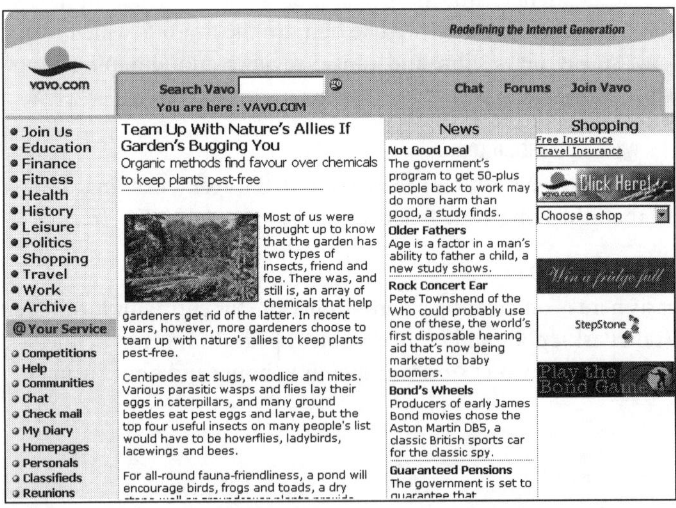

■ *The rest of the best*

Retirement Matters **www.retirement-matters.co.uk**
A slightly cluttered but extremely useful site packed with information, advice and links for retired people. We especially like Derek Jameson's musings on the world.

Hairnet **www.hairnet.org**
Hairnet offers hands-on computer training to the over-50s and, although it mainly operates in London, there are expert trainers all over the UK ready to help you get the most out of your PC – all from the comfort of your own home. Also see the excellent My Hairnet (**www.myhairnet.com**) for a wealth of over-50s information.

Silver Surfers **www.silversurfers.net**
If you haven't managed to find something suitable on one of the over-50s portals then a quick visit to Silver Surfers is probably in order. Cluttered but useful.

Sites for lesbians and gay men

■ *The best of the best*

About Gay Life **gaylife.about.com**
Another excellent site from About.com, this time focusing on a wide range of gay and lesbian issues through well-written articles, forums, polls and links to the best of the web. It's based in America and so some of the information may not be totally relevant to UK visitors, but there's more than enough to point you in the right direction.

■ *The rest of the best*

Gay Life UK **www.gaylifeuk.com**
A whole host of UK-based gay features including pub and club listings, support pages, news, a chat room, financial information and links to relevant sites and resources. For a more American perspective, check out the ultra-slick Planet Out (**www.planetout.com**).

Lesbian Nation **www.lesbianation.com**

As the name suggests, this excellent American site is just for the girls. Extremely high production values are the name of the game here, with extremely well-written content to ensure that it's not a case of form over function.

Gay.com **uk.gay.com**

This British version of one of the US's most popular gay resources aims to connect 'the UK lesbian, gay, bisexual and transgender communities' – and, if the quality of articles and range of features on offer are anything to go by, it's doing a pretty good job.

■ *The best of the rest*

Gay Times **www.gaytimes.co.uk**

A whole world of useful resources, designed for a UK audience.

Queer Resources Directory **www.qrd.org**

A no-holds-barred directory of online gay and lesbian content – and with over 25,000 files listed, you're bound to find something of interest.

It's an unfortunate fact of life that things don't always go according to plan. You've probably heard the alarming statistic that one in three marriages ends in divorce – and plenty of those that don't will hit a rocky patch at some point. Even if your marriage is rock-steady, families can be hit with legal problems, money worries and bereavement and, while the internet can't offer a solution, there are plenty of sites to help you through those difficult times, or at least put you in touch with experts who can. Financial and legal advice are covered in Chapters 3 and 6, respectively.

Marriage and relationship advice

■ *The best of the best*

Marriage Care **www.marriagecare.org.uk**

Marriage Care is a registered charity with one main purpose – to safeguard the

institution of marriage and its meaning in today's society. In order to help couples who might have run into problems and advise those who haven't yet tied the knot, it has created an excellent resource packed full of help, support, reassurance and a wealth of advice on building and maintaining a strong family.

The rest of the best

Relate **www.relate.org.uk**

Relate is probably the best-known organisation in the field of relationship counselling and although its site is not as slick as Marriage Care, you'll find plenty of information on the organisation itself, what it can do for you and how to find your nearest counselling centre.

Divorce Online **www.divorce-online.co.uk**

It's a messy process, but this site couldn't be slicker. Advice and self-help information will guide you in making the right decision, while downloadable divorce packs make it frighteningly easy to get unhitched.

Divorce.co.uk **www.divorce.co.uk**

Divorce.co.uk aims to help families 'manage their way through marriage breakdown, separation and divorce' and covers thorny issues such as deciding to end the relationship and telling your children, as well as offering practical advice and links to legal information.

Bereavement advice

The best of the best

London Bereavement Network **www.bereavement.org.uk**

From practical advice on how to deal with the death of a loved one to academic discussion on the psychological effects of bereavement, the site covers almost everything you could want (or need) to know.

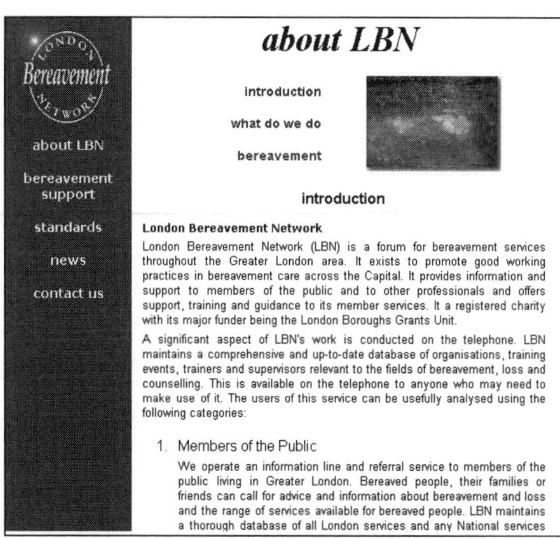

The rest of the best

The Centre for Grief Education **www.grief.org.au**

Australian site offering information about the centre itself, as well as some extremely useful links to grief and bereavement sites on the internet.

15 genealogy

You might know everything there is to know about your immediate family, but what about those long-lost relatives and distant ancestors? No matter whether you are related to a famous historical character or that bloke who Francis Drake told to shove off until he'd finished his game of bowls – the internet makes it easier than ever to track them down.

Genealogy portals

■ *The best of the best*

Cyndi's List **www.cyndislist.com**

We must confess to being a little concerned about Cyndi. Not only is she clearly obsessed with genealogy, but she has also taken the time to collect and categorise

over 73,000 online genealogy resources. Not that we're complaining, of course, as the site makes it easier than ever to find the information you need – using over 120 categories from unique peoples and cultures to ships' passenger lists and national dress. In short, if it's not here, you're not going to find it anywhere else.

The rest of the best

Family Search **www.familysearch.org**

If Cyndi's List is all just a little too much for you, you might prefer the slick user-friendliness of Family Search from the Church of the Latter Day Saints. Using the service couldn't be easier: you simply type in as much information as possible about the person you're looking for and their immediate family and click the 'Search' button. If you get a match then it's a simple matter of choosing the records you need and downloading them to your computer. Job done.

Ancestry **www.ancestry.com**

The well-presented and utterly huge database of genealogy information makes it pretty straightforward to track down your Uncle Fred, no matter when or where he lived. The only minor drawbacks are the American bias of the information and the fact that you have to pay for the results. It's great – if you don't mind parting with a few quid.

Family History **www.familyhistory.com**

Over 100,000 message boards, each focusing on a particular surname or set of surnames. Once you've tracked down your family board it's straightforward enough to start asking around for the information you need.

UK-specific resources

The best of the best

GENUKI **www.genuki.org.uk**

Well-written guides to tracing relatives, information on genealogy in general and an extremely thorough set of links to relevant material and resources make this an essential port of call for experienced and first-time genealogists alike.

The rest of the best

The Society of Genealogists **www.sog.org.uk**

As the name of the site suggests, this is the official online home of a group of people who know one or two things about tracking down ancestors. Generously, they've decided to share some of this knowledge with the rest of us in the form of well-written publications, information leaflets and, of course, this website.

Scots Origins **www.origins.net**

Scots Origins is the official governmental source of genealogical data for Scotland and, although there is a small charge for using the service, the huge amount of information on offer makes it well worth the money. It looks pretty sharp, too.

The best of the rest

The Commonwealth War Graves Commission **www.cwgc.org**

Their name liveth evermore. Moving and informative in equal measure.

National Statistics **www.statistics.gov.uk**

The official source of information relating to hatches, matches and dispatches.

pets and animals 16

Just because they have four legs instead of two doesn't make them any the less a part of the family. If you don't have pets you probably won't understand – but if you do, this one's for you.

Animal advice

■ *The best of the best*

RSPCA **www.rspca.org.uk**
This bright and friendly site from the RSPCA contains a wealth of information about animals of all sizes, from domestic cats to endangered monkeys. Also, if you're not sure if you want the responsibility of looking after a pet, you can adopt a virtual one to try before you buy. For slightly bigger animals, check out Born Free (**www.bornfree.org.uk**).

The rest of the best

Complete Hamster Site **www.hamsters.co.uk**

If you love hamsters, you can't help but love this shrine to the little wheel runners. There's a hamster e-zine, hamster facts, hamster pictures, hamster advice, hamster clubs and even a run-down of products for … yes, you've guessed it, hamsters. For hamster fun without the straw and mess, check out Hamster Dance (**www.nuttysites.com/rodent**).

Pet Cat **www.petcat.com**

Feline lovers rejoice! Pet Cat contains everything you could possibly need to look after your cat. From virtual cat adoption and exclusive cat news to a yearly cat diary and e-kitty cards, it's a little obsessive but fun nonetheless.

Equiworld **www.equiworld.net**

If you love horses, you simply have to visit Equiworld, with its care and breeding information, horsey news, sporty stuff and loads more for both budding and existing riders. A definite winner for fans of the animals as well as the sports. For more of the same, see Equine World (**www.equine-world.co.uk**).

The best of the rest

Dogs Online	**www.dogsonline.co.uk**
Fish Keeping	**www.fishkeeping.co.uk**
UK Pet Rabbits	**www.ukpet.rabbits.org.uk**

Online pet shops

The best of the best

Pet Planet **www.petplanet.co.uk**

So much more than a pet shop, Pet Planet offer loads of information and advice on looking after pets, as well as a virtual vet who will be happy to answer your animal health questions.

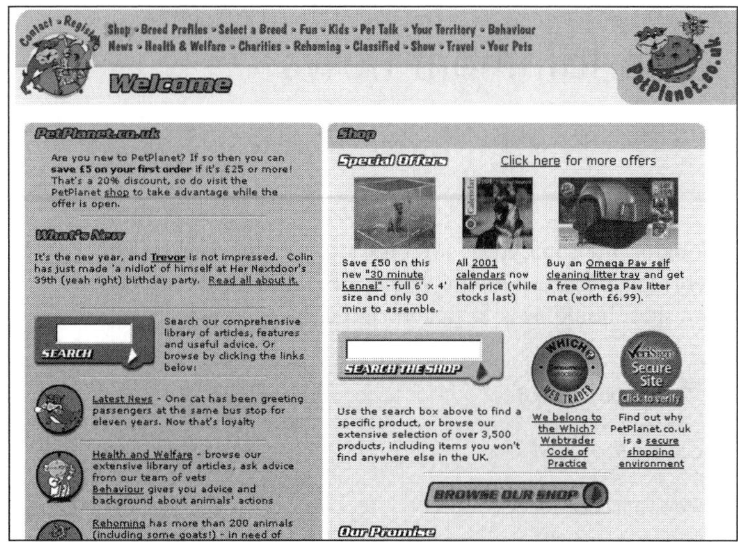

■ *The rest of the best*

Petspark www.petspark.co.uk

Catering for cats and dogs, Petspark offers a decent range of toys, accessories and food to suit almost any breed and, more importantly, any budget.

Blue Pet www.bluepet.co.uk

Another pet shop, another silly name. Blue Pet is a beautifully designed emporium of dog- and cat-related stuff, including healthy food, natural remedies, stylish collars and unique toys. The cat's whiskers.

Petplan Equine www.petplanequine.co.uk

Petplan Equine from Cornhill Insurance offers a range of insurance packages for horses and ponies. The site will give you a quote but, at the time of writing, you couldn't order online.

17 entertainment news

If you're looking for some ideas for things to do this weekend or want to know which celebrities are in or out of rehab, one of our recommended portals and information sites should be your first port of call.

Listings and reviews

The best of the best

Virgin Net **www.virgin.net**

Branson's quest for world domination continues with this massive resource which makes finding cinema listings, TV schedules, pubs, clubs, restaurants, theatres, days

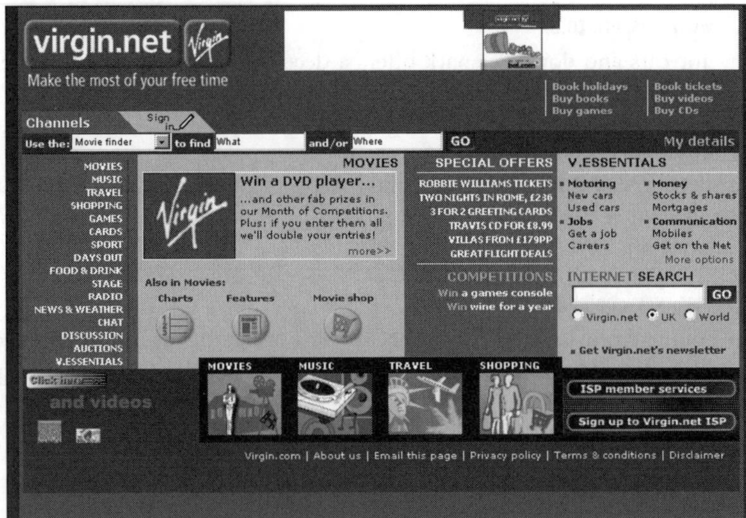

out, shops – and even romance – easier than it's ever been before. The layout of the site is busy but not cluttered and, with search boxes aplenty, you'll find it pretty straightforward to find what you're looking for.

The rest of the best

Scene One **www.sceneone.co.uk**

While Scene One may not be as ambitious as Virgin Net – it restricts itself to entertainment rather than trying to cover everything to do with leisure – its content is certainly no less impressive. Film, music, television, books and comedy are covered with a slightly irreverent tone which manages to inform as well as amuse and, with online purchasing of tickets and products, the site certainly makes the most of the technology.

Celebrities

The best of the best

E! Online **www.eonline.com**

For the latest in American showbiz gossip, look no further than E! Online, the web's finest rumour mill. Ah, show business, there's no business like it. For more of the same, check out eDrive (**www.edrive.com**).

The rest of the best

Celebsites **www.celebsites.com**

From Antonio Banderas to Zena the Warrior Princess, this well stocked directory of over 20,000 celebrity fan sites makes it a simple matter to track down information on your favourite star. If you're searching for British celebrities or famous B-list folk, you'll probably have better luck with one of the specialist film or music sites – but if you're looking for shrines to the beautiful people, they're all here.

Hot Gossip **www.hotgossip.com**

Celebrity gossip just got a whole lot more interactive, thanks to the ubergirlie shrine to hearsay that is Hot Gossip. Nice but dim.

Dead People Server **www.dpsinfo.com**

We've all had arguments over whether a particular star is still shining or whether they have gone to that great cutting room in the sky. As luck would have it, Dead People Server allows you to settle this type of argument once and for all by listing a wealth of celebrities along with either the date of their demise or a reassurance that they're still very much alive and kicking. All in the best possible taste.

Mr Showbiz **www.mrshowbiz.go.com**

Mr Showbiz (Showbiz to his friends) certainly doesn't hold back when it comes to gossip and rumour-mongering. American visitors will definitely get more out of the site than British folk, but if you don't want the facts to get in the way of a good story, you'll love it.

music and radio 18

From Elvis to the Eurythmics, David Bowie to Daphne and Celeste, Bach to Birtwistle – no matter what your taste in music, there are millions of people online who share it. Or, in the case of Daphne and Celeste, make that tens of people. There are sites dedicated to opera, jazz, pop, rock, country and western, rap, hip-hop, ballet – even line dancing – as well as music download sites, internet radio stations and so much more. Music on the web? We know where it's at.

Portals and news

■ *The best of the best*

Dot Music **www.dotmusic.co.uk**

There's a definite sense of community at Dot Music which, as well as offering the

latest news, gig reviews and celebrity gossip, has a huge number of forums dedicated to different artists and groups. Through the live news feeds and discussion boards you can find out about everyone from The Beatles to Limp Bizkit and, shrewd business people that they are, Dot Music also allows you to order music directly from the site. Opera fans may be a little disappointed by the site's bias towards chart stuff, but if you like to keep your finger on the pulse of the music business, it's never been easier.

■ *The rest of the best*

World Pop **www.worldpop.com**

The official sponsor of the UK charts has produced a suitably official-looking site which is bursting at the seams with news, information and features. Whereas Dot Music concentrates on its community aspect, World Pop seems intent on milking its relationship with the charts for all it's worth through celebrity interviews, news and reviews.

All Music **www.allmusic.com**

Striking a blow for musical diversity, All Music offers a searchable guide to the complete spectrum of genres. Being an American site, you'll have more luck finding US artists, but the depth of coverage is truly amazing and, if you're looking for something outside the top 40, this should definitely be your first port of call.

Pepsi Chart **www.networkchart.com**

Speaking of the top 40, the online home of Dr Fox is one of the first places to announce each week's run-down, complete with background information, celebrity interviews and gossip. This being the official Pepsi Chart site, it's a front-running contender for our 'most sycophantic music site on the web' award, so don't expect any gossip the record companies don't want you to hear – but it's well worth a look nonetheless.

NME.com **www.nme.com**

All the usual news and gig reviews are here, plus general and band-specific bulletin boards allowing you to meet and argue with other fans – but that's not all. The NME shop is packed to the rafters with ... erm ... music, while NME.com Gigs (**www.nme.com/gigs**) is the place to go for access to the UK's hottest gigs and festivals.

Q Online **www.Q4.com**

NME is not the only music magazine storming the web, as *Q* magazine's official effort ably demonstrates. The content is not wildly different from the other music sites, but the vast archive of features from previous issues makes it something of a music lover's dream.

Music365 **www.music365.com**

Unfortunately, competitors like Dot Music and NME.com are that little bit too good to be beaten into second place by Music365's impressive but slightly cluttered blend of news, reviews and features. Having said that, the site is still incredibly impressive and is certainly well worth a look.

Addicted to Noise **www.addict.com**

Hi everyone, my name's Bob and I'm a soundaholic.

Channel Fly **www.channelfly.com**

Ultra-cool UK music site. Also offering free subs to its equally impressive paper version.

The best of the rest

Classical Net	**www.classical.net**	MTV	**www.mtv.com**
Classic FM	**www.classicfm.co.uk**	Opera Base	**www.operabase.com**
Click Music	**www.clickmusic.co.uk**	Rolling Stone	**www.rollingstone.com**
Global Music Network	**www.gmn.com**	Top of the Pops	**www.totp.beeb.com**
Juno	**www.juno.co.uk**		

Artists

The best of the best

The Ultimate Band List **www.ubl.com**

Why waste hours looking for information about your favourite band when The Ultimate Band List will guide you straight to a whole world of official and unofficial shrines to your heroes? From Van Halen to Vanilla Ice, this vast directory features a

huge number of artistes, covering the complete musical spectrum, and there's also a well-stocked shop plus some well-written content from UBL itself. Rock on.

The rest of the best

Abba	**www.abbasite.com**
Aerosmith	**www.aerosmith.com**
Del Amitri	**www.delamitri.com**
Backstreet Boys	**www.backstreetboys.com**
Blur	**www.blur.co.uk**
David Bowie	**www.davidbowie.com**
Craig David	**www.craigdavid.co.uk**
Bob Dylan	**www.bobdylan.com**
Garbage	**www.garbage.net**
Public Enemy	**www.public-enemy.com**
REM	**www.murmers.com**
The Rolling Stones	**www.the-rolling-stones.com**
Semisonic	**www.semisonic.com**
Hootie and the Blowfish	**www.hootie.com**
Michael Jackson	**www.mjnet.com**
Madonna	**www.madonnamusic.com**
Barry Manilow	**www.barrynet.com**
Bob Marley	**www.bobmarley.com**
George Michael	**www.aegean.net**
Kylie Minogue	**www.kylie.com**
Oasis	**www.oasisinet.com**
Elvis Presley	**www.elvis-presley.com**
Will Smith	**www.willsmith.net**
Britney Spears	**www.britney.com**
Travis Online	**www.travisonline.com**
Robbie Williams	**www.robbiewilliams.co.uk**

Festivals and clubbing

The best of the best

Virtual Festivals **www.virtual-festivals.com**

There's a lot to be said for Virtual Festivals. After all, you can get (almost) the whole festival experience but without the mud, scary toilets and getting your tent nicked. Festival guides from the UK, Europe and Japan, star interviews, photo galleries, message boards and even a girlie guide make this an essential bookmark. We like.

The rest of the best

i-gig **www.i-gig.com**

Want to attend live gigs without leaving your house? Suit yourself – simply zip over to i-gig and enjoy some of today's hottest acts playing live on your desktop.

Clubber **www.clubber.co.uk**

Clubber is one of the few dance music sites which manage to capture the atmosphere of the club scene without the commercialism of sites like Ministry of

Sound (see below). Hardcore. You know the score. On the dancefloor. You want some more? Maybe later.

Club Net **www.clubnet-uk.com**

Right from the opening page, Club Net bombards you with enough sound and motion to make a Jean Michel Jarre concert look like a school disco. Basically, it's a guide to clubs around the UK, separated into regions, with a huge list of venues and some basic contact info for each. If you're planning a night out in an unfamiliar town, you'll definitely want to check out your options here.

Beach Beats **www.beachbeats.com**

If your idea of holiday heaven is a fortnight in the clubs and bars of Ibiza or Ayia Napa, then this site was designed for you. Alongside club guides and features from the likes of *Kiss100* and *Mixmag*, there's weather information, travel tips and some excellent travel bargains. Smooth.

Ministry of Sound **www.ministryofsound.com**

Quite possibly the most famous club of them all, Ministry of Sound has spawned numerous albums and items of shiny clothing as well as launching many a DJ on to the world stage. Unsurprisingly, the site is a little commercialised – but Ministry fans will definitely love the chat rooms, webcams and general clubbing news. For more of the same, there's no place like Home (**www.homecorp.co.uk**).

Radio

■ *The best of the best*

RealGuide **europe.real.com/guide**

RealPlayer is the undisputed king of audio and video streaming software – but once you've downloaded it you'll want something to listen to or watch, which is where the RealGuide comes in. Simply type in what you're looking for, by country, subject or language, for a complete run-down of your listening and viewing options.

■ *The rest of the best*

Internet Radio List **www.internetradiolist.com**

The Internet Radio List is a truly global guide to live internet audio broadcasts. Simply choose the type of music you're looking for, or search by country, and you'll find a whole host of suitable broadcasts, some live, some pre-recorded.

BBC Radio **www.bbc.co.uk/radio**

Join Terry Wogan and his broadcasting buddies on the extremely slick official BBC Radio site. As you'd expect from the UK's leading broadcaster, you can listen online using RealPlayer, plus there's tons of background information, programme listings and a great mix of music, from classical to dance.

Capital Online **www.capitalfm.com**

The latest music news and reviews as well as DJ profiles, competitions, daily polls, discussion forums, exclusive features and more. If you don't live in London then you can still enjoy the Capital experience by listening to it over the web – including Dr Fox's weekly Pepsi Chart show.

Virgin Radio **www.virginradio.com**
The shows, the DJs and, of course, the music are all covered in impressive detail, with competitions, features and interviews to keep you coming back for more.

Storm Live **www.stormlive.com**
As one of Europe's first internet-only radio stations, Storm Live's playlist may be a bit 'lowest common denominator' for some – but if you're getting bored with Capital and want some music to surf the web by, you'll love it.

Gogaga **www.gogaga.com**
It's a difficult enough job to produce fresh and entertaining content on the web, but to achieve that while also pumping out the best online radio is nothing short of genius. If you're looking for something you won't hear on your car radio, drop everything and go ga ga. Love it.

■ *The best of the rest*

About Internet Radio **internetradio.about.com**
The complete low-down on internet radio, including guides to the programmes, the technology, the personalities and, of course, the music.

Computer Music **www.computer-music.co.uk/internet.htm**
Providing access to some of Europe's best online audio content, including live broadcasts from top UK radio stations.

interFACE **interface.pirate-radio.co.uk**
Despite the fact that you can't actually have pirate radio stations on the web, interFACE is probably the nearest thing the web has to underground broadcasting. At the time of writing the station wasn't broadcasting 24 hours a day, but if you miss a live set then you can always listen to pre-recorded material from the previous night.

Kerbango **www.kerbango.com**
Offering a complete searchable guide to online radio and an incredibly funky piece of hardware to play it on.

Kiss100 **www.kiss100.co.uk**

The dance music station for young London encourages you to 'stay sexy' with possibly the brightest radio site on the web.

Shoutcast **www.shoutcast.com**

Want to set up your own station – or just listen to everyone else's efforts? You'll need Shoutcast then.

Student Broadcast Network **www.sbn.co.uk**

You don't have to be a student to enjoy student radio. In fact, thanks to SBN, you don't even need a radio.

vTuner **www.vtuner.com**

Scans the web for live radio broadcasts. Apparently.

Downloads

■ *The best of the best*

Napster **www.napster.com**

Bit of a tricky one this – although Napster claims to be a place where unsigned bands can swap MP3s with potential fans, at the time of writing Napster was busy

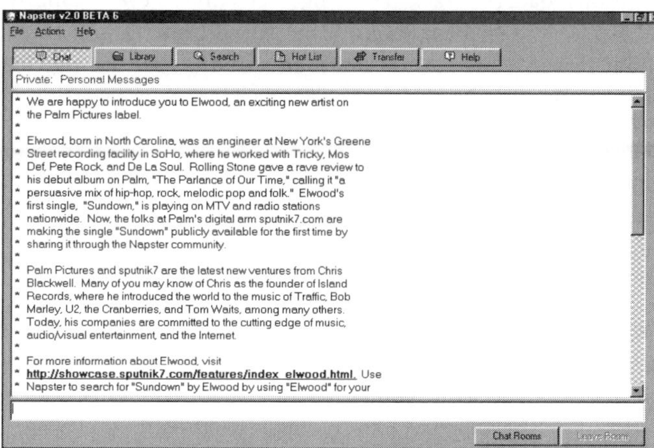

signing deals with major record companies to avoid messy copyright lawsuits. Basically, Napster effectively turns part of your hard drive into a storage bank of MP3 music while allowing you to search other Napster users' computers for tracks that you might be interested in. This community of music swapping has inevitably led to claims of rampant copyright infringement, with users converting their CD collection into MP3 format and making it freely available to the rest of the world. But, whatever your views on piracy, the software is a work of pure genius and it's a great way for new artists to get their music heard. Oh, by the way, if you get there and find a subscription-based service then it's probably sold out to the big boys.

The rest of the best

Peoplesound **www.peoplesound.com**

If Napster is a bit too controversial for your tastes, then Peoplesound is a totally legit way to hear new and unsigned artists from the comfort of your computer. Dance, pop, rock, indie, classical, easy listening, hip-hop, jazz, new age, R&B, reggae, world – no matter what your musical tastes, you're bound to find something of interest; and if you're not sure what you want, simply type in the name of your favourite famous artist and Peoplesound will suggest similar unsigned alternatives.

MP3.com **www.mp3.com**

The site which started the whole MP3 download craze is still going strong, with thousands of downloadable tracks covering pretty much every conceivable genre. Unlike the UK's very own Peoplesound, the site is American so you can expect plenty of guitar-driven garage bands, but there's so much music here that you can't fail to find something you like.

Vitaminic **www.vitaminic.co.uk**

Despite sounding like a health food shop, Vitaminic is actually snapping at the heels of Peoplesound as our favourite legal music download site. All the styles are here, there are thousands of free tracks to be downloaded and budding music superstars can sell their music online. Impressive stuff.

Channel Fly **www.channelfly.com**

Downloadable tracks from some of the UK's hottest bands plus a wealth of news, features and live events make Channel Fly an essential bookmark for music fans. Pretty fly.

iCrunch **www.icrunch.com**
Rather than trying to be all things to all music fans, iCrunch concentrates on alternative, breaks, trance, leftfield, drum and bass, house and techno. No Des O'Connor then. It's not a free-for-all either – most tracks have a price tag attached, although with music starting at just 99p, it's hardly going to break the bank.

Get Out There **getoutthere.bt.com**
British Telecom is not exactly synonymous with the world of music and film but, if Get Out There is anything to go by, there's definitely scope for diversification. The formula is instantly recognisable – up and coming artists and directors can promote their work through the site and we can download it for free.

Still hungry for more? For the best legal (and not so legal) MP3 tracks on the web, Lycos (**mp3.lycos.com**) is the place to start searching.

Music players

■ *The best of the best*

RealPlayer **www.real.com**
It's a bit redundant to recommend RealPlayer as, in order to play most types of

streaming audio and video content, it is absolutely essential. There's not much more to say other than, if you haven't already, download this superb music player now – and, while you're at it, make sure you also download QuickTime (**www.quicktime.com**).

The rest of the best

Music Match **www.musicmatch.com**

Having just said that the best players are free, Music Match is an exception to the rule. This feature-packed player does ask you to pay a small registration fee if you want to make the most of its many features – but with advanced music management tools, CD burning, cover printing, MP3 creation and so much more, it's worth every single penny. Highly recommended.

Sonique **www.sonique.com**

It's free, it's extremely funky and it plays music. Nuff said.

Music shopping

The best of the best

Audiostreet **www.audiostreet.co.uk**

You can't fail to be impressed by this extremely well-stocked site from Streets Online. The UK top 40 are all present and correct, and it's not too shoddy on the old stuff either. One of the first UK stores to offer music DVDs.

The rest of the best

101 CD **www.101cd.com**

Operated from a conventional high street music shop, 101 offers a truly massive range of CDs to suit every conceivable musical taste. The real selling point here, though, is that 101 is able to get hold of hard-to-find albums by importing them from Europe and America. Yes, you wait a bit longer for some of the more obscure titles, but when you've already spent weeks looking for something, it's a price worth paying.

The best of the rest

CD Wow **www.cdwow.co.uk**

Don dark glasses and try not to look directly at the screen when you visit CD Wow. The prices are certainly low and there's a decent range available, but someone needs to have a word about the use of the colour yellow. Blinding.

Replay **www.replay.co.uk**

If you're a DJ (or older than 14) this could be your idea of heaven. Specialising in rare vinyl, Replay has a great range of dance, jazz, rock and reggae albums and a few singles thrown in for good measure. Dig deep enough and you'll find some true classics. If you're still looking try Hard to Find (**www.hard-to-find.co.uk**) or, for more dancy stuff, check out Ministry of Sound (**www.ministryofsound.co.uk**).

19 film

Whatever type of films you prefer, fire up your PC and get online – the latest movie news and gossip, cinema listings, downloadable trailers and a whole world of film-related content are all just a mouse click away. For video and DVD, see Shopping.

News and reviews

■ *The best of the best*

Popcorn **www.popcorn.co.uk**

Popcorn is an essential bookmark for anyone even remotely interested in films, with its mix of news, reviews, gossip, downloadable trailers and a superbly useful

searchable cinemas listings system. Simply select your local cinema and you'll get a complete run-down of what's on at what time, cross-referenced to the site's excellent reviews and features.

■ *The rest of the best*

Empire Online **www.empireonline.co.uk**

If you need another review to back up Popcorn's opinion of a particular movie, then you won't do much better than the online edition of *Empire* magazine. In addition to all the news, reviews, interviews and other content you'd expect to find in the paper version, there's a very useful searchable archive of reviews, a cinema guide and a well-stocked online movie shop.

Ain't It Cool News **www.aint-it-cool-news.com**

Don't let the cluttered design put you off, Ain't It Cool News is without doubt the most influential and up-to-date movie news site on the planet. Being an American site, combined with the fact that it's so far ahead of the game, means that most of the news is about films you may not even have heard of – but trust us when we say that if Harry Knowles slates a movie, directors and stars sit up and listen.

Total Film **www.totalfilm.co.uk**

The web version of *Total Film* magazine is intended to complement rather than replace the paper version, with reviews of the latest releases as well as an impressive array of celebrity interviews and an archive of the best bits from previous issues.

BBC Films **www.bbc.co.uk/films**

OK, it hasn't been the same since Barry Norman defected to satellite, but the BBC's *Film* programme has always been essential viewing for film buffs. Fortunately, the official BBC Films site is just as entertaining as the programme, with behind-the-scenes news, interviews and more reviews than you can shake an Oscar at.

Mr Cranky **www.mrcranky.com**

Who needs Barry Norman or Jonathan Ross when you've got Mr Cranky? The internet's most grouchy film critic is never happier than when he's tearing a new release apart with a few well-chosen words – and in Cranky world no film is good, it's simply less bad than the others. It probably gives you an idea of what to expect when we tell you that the rating system goes from the positively glowing 'almost tolerable' to the downright abysmal 'so godawful that it ruptured the very fabric of space and time with the sheer overpowering force of its mediocrity'. Cranky by name …

■ *The best of the rest*

6degrees **www.6degrees.co.uk**
Monthly guide to the best independent films on UK release. Very well put together and certainly some of the most intelligent reviews we've found.

Blunt Review **www.bluntreview.com**
Self-appointed film critic Emily Blunt (you see?) reviews the latest US releases with a surprisingly non-blunt style. We're not sure about some of the awful films which received glowing reviews, but you'll probably want to make up your own mind.

Film Festivals **www.filmfestivals.com**
Dark and moody guide to international film festivals and independent film-makers, and an extremely thorough round-up of movie news and release dates covering most of Europe and the USA.

Film Review **www.filmreview.co.uk**
Well-put-together answer to the web's more American film review sites.

Film Unlimited **www.filmunlimited.co.uk**
Another winner from the *Guardian*, Film Unlimited offers reviews of the latest releases plus a whole world of movie news. First class.

Movie Review Query Engine **www.mrqe.com**
Search a vast database of reviews covering over 17,000 films.

Screen Daily **www.screendaily.com**
Provides a UK perspective on both film production and the slightly less glamorous world of film distribution. A real eye opener.

The Oscars **www.oscar.com**

Everything you need to know about Tinsel Town's most prestigious awards ceremony. Hooray for Hollywood.

Variety **www.variety.com**

A more Hollywood-friendly version of Ain't It Cool News.

Information and trivia

■ *The best of the best*

The Internet Movie Database **www.imdb.com**

If you want film information and trivia then there really is only one place to come. The IMDB started out as a small database of movies and actors, but has since become the world's biggest and finest film information site. There are over 200,000 cinema and TV film titles to search, with info about the plot, the actors, the rating, the directors and pretty much everything else you could want to know. Love it.

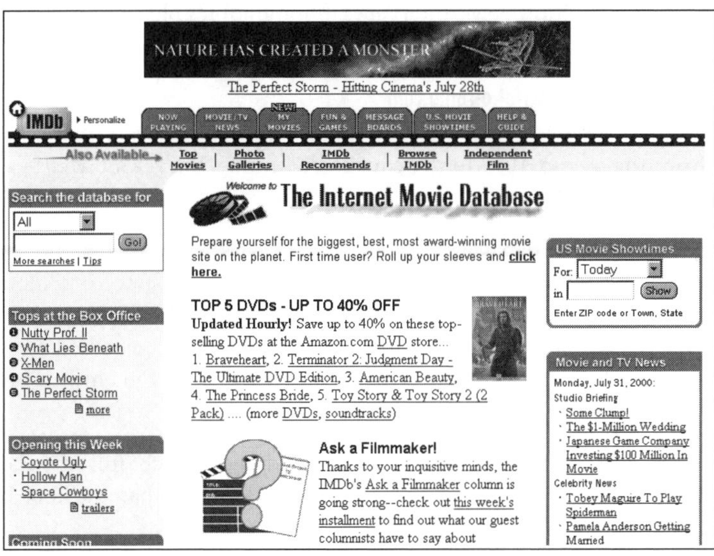

The rest of the best

All Movie Guide **www.allmovie.com**

From the people who brought you the All Music Guide comes this extremely comprehensive guide to the world of film. From 1960s classics to today's blockbusters, you'll find reviews, cast and crew profiles, and enough background information to satisfy even the most obsessive film fan. No matter whether you want to find out about the cast of *Casablanca* or the crew of *A Clockwork Orange*, it's all here – it's just a shame that the TV listings information is only useful for American visitors.

The Film 100 **www.film100.com**

Ranking the 100 most influential people in the history of cinema is an impressive enough feat in itself, but the real beauty of The Film 100 is the way in which it justifies its choices by offering a complete run-down of each list member's contribution to the industry as well as other useful trivia about some true movie icons.

The British Film Institute **www.momi.co.uk**

The official site of the BFI is an independent cinema fan's dream, with film and cinema listings, exhibition news, interviews, filmographies plus, of course, plenty of in-depth features covering classic and modern British films.

Drew's Script O Rama **www.script-o-rama.com**

Script O Rama contains the original scripts for just about every major film ever made – from the classic *Alien* to the equally disturbing *You've Got Mail* – all freely available for download.

Movie Cliches **www.moviecliches.com**

Have you ever noticed how James Bond always effortlessly escapes from 'inescapable' traps? And that photos of loved ones, religious medals and bibles can stop bullets better than a bulletproof vest? These, and hundreds of other cinematic observations, can be found at Movie Cliches, which we guarantee will keep you amused for hours.

Movie Mistakes **www.movie-mistakes.com**

If Movie Mistakes is anything to go by, the world is obviously full of people with plenty of time on their hands who enjoy nothing better than picking holes in thousands of popular films.

British Board of Film Classification **www.bbfc.co.uk**

Ever wondered why your favourite film was given an 18 rating or what the BBFC thought about some of the world's most controversial movies? The answers are all on this fascinating official site.

Oh, the Humanity! **www.ohthehumanity.com**

A handy guide to some of the world's most earth-shatteringly dreadful films.

Film Bug **www.filmbug.com**

A no-frills, information-packed cornucopia of movie news, information, trivia and celebrity profiles. Includes thousands of links to official and unofficial sites.

Still searching for a star? They're all at Celebsites (**www.celebsites.com**).

Films and studios

■ *The best of the best*

Universal Exports **www.universalexports.net**

Named after the company James Bond pretended to work for while undercover,

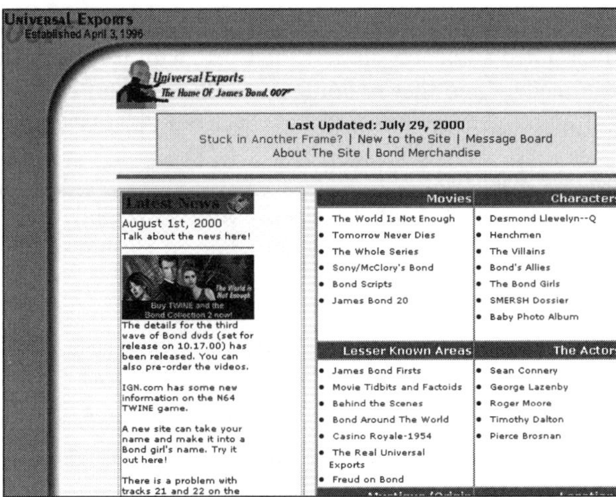

Universal Exports is a classic example of what makes a good fan site. From the in-depth character profiles, film synopses and run-down of the gadgets to the regular updates, news and gossip, this well-designed unofficial site puts the official effort to shame. If, however, you want the official story, check out James Bond.com (**www.jamesbond.com**). Quite simply 00-heaven.

The rest of the best

The Force **www.theforce.net**

Just in case you hadn't already guessed, The Force is dedicated to all things *Star Wars*. Although the site is completely unofficial, it really is the first (and possibly only) place to go for the latest news, behind-the-scenes information, features and downloads. The official site's at Star Wars (**www.starwars.com**) by the way.

Disney **www.disney.co.uk**

Can you imagine a world without Disney? No Mickey Mouse, no Donald Duck, no Toy Story, no overpriced merchandise. Nightmare. Games, screen savers, movie news, trailers and, of course, tons of excellent animation make for a thoroughly entertaining surfing session for all the family.

Aardman Animations **www.aardman.com**

Wallace and Gromit, Chicken Run – the gang's all here. Nick Park's little animated chums have entertained audiences all over the world with their very British style of clay-modelled comedy – and they're doing an excellent job of carrying on the fun online. For a computer-generated alternative, check out Pixar (**www.pixar.com**).

Cyberblanca **www.cyberblanca.com**

If you're looking for a truly quotable classic, you won't find much better than *Casablanca* – and if it's unofficial info you're after, of all the websites, on all the servers, on all the web, you'll want to surf into this one.

The best of the rest

Dreamworks	**www.dreamworks.com**	Lucasfilm	**www.lucasfilm.com**
Fox Movies	**www.foxmovies.com**	MGM	**www.mgm.com**

Miramax **www.miramax.com**
Paramount **www.paramount.com**
Sony **www.spe.sony.com**
Universal Studios **www.mca.com**
Warner Brothers **www.warnerbrothers.com**

Downloads and live video

■ *The best of the best*

ifilm **www.ifilm.net**

Whether you're looking for blockbuster movies or the finest independent film-making, ifilm will deliver it all directly to your desktop. Simply choose the film you want to watch, grab some virtual popcorn, sit back and enjoy – and once the final credits have rolled, there's still plenty more to see, including movie news, reviews, interviews, a beginner's guide to film-making and a superb collection of links to other related sites.

■ *The rest of the best*

Get Out There **getoutthere.bt.com**

For the best in new British film-making talent, look no further than this nifty site from BT. Once you've finished checking out the films, there's plenty of advice to help you start making your own. Nice.

The Sync **www.thesync.com**

The Sync claims to offer video for the net generation – and it's doing a pretty good job, too. There may not be the sheer volume of material offered by ifilm – nevertheless the phrase 'quality over quantity' springs instantly to mind when you look at the great range of films and virtual TV shows, all available completely free of charge. Particular highlights include the virtual film festival, IndExposure, and the thoroughly enjoyable JenniShow, starring Jennifer Ringley of JenniCAM (**www.jennicam.com**) fame.

Movie List **www.movie-list.com**

If you've got a fast modem you'll love Movie List, which allows you to download the latest movie trailers, free of charge, for your entertainment and pleasure. If, on the other hand, you don't have a fast modem, you'll probably still love it – just less often.

Cinemas and listings

■ *The best of the best*

Scoot Cinema Guide **www.cinema.scoot.co.uk**

Simply the finest film finder on the web. Not only does the Scoot Cinema Guide

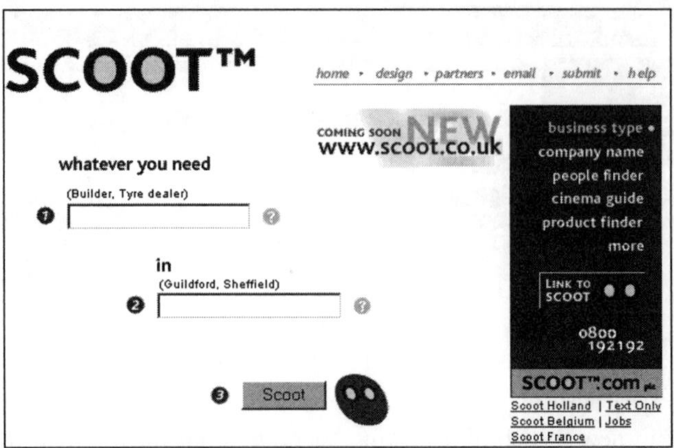

allow you to search by location or film title, but it will also provide a brief review of the films on offer, directions to the cinema and even a complete run-down on the facilities provided. It's extremely fast, bang up to date, easy to use and absolutely indispensable. Bookmark it now – you'll be glad you did.

■ *The rest of the best*

Odeon Cinemas **www.odeon.co.uk**
Odeon Cinemas may not, generally, be the most modern in the business – but when it comes to the web, it's streets ahead of the rest. Not only can you find your nearest cinema and check out what's showing but – and this is the good bit – you can book tickets online to avoid those nasty queues.

UCI Cinemas **www.uci-cinemas.com**
It may not be able to hold a candle to Odeon's superb effort but the official UCI site has a lot going for it. Find out what's on at your nearest multiplex, read all about new releases and even get travel directions which take into account the direction you're coming from.

Yell Film Finder **www.yell.co.uk/yell/ff**
The online edition of the Yellow Pages (Yell to its friends) has made a pretty good attempt at matching Scoot's cinema guide service but, unfortunately, it doesn't quite pull it off with as much panache. It's a good place to find a second opinion though.

■ *The best of the rest*

ABC Cinemas	**www.abc-cinemas.co.uk**	Warner Village	**www.warnervillage.co.uk**
Showcase Cinemas	**www.showcasecinemas.co.uk**		

Video and DVD shopping

■ *The best of the best*

Blackstar **www.blackstar.co.uk**
If you've ever ordered from Blackstar you'll know that there could be no

competition for the best of the best video and DVD retailer. Its stock is truly huge, but that's not all – excellent service, excellent prices, intelligent reviews, clear yet stylish design and prompt delivery make Blackstar one of the web's true retail success stories.

The rest of the best

Filmworld **www.filmworld.co.uk**

Making an informed purchase couldn't be simpler at Filmworld, which provides extremely detailed background information about every film it stocks. Browsing is simple enough, but if you want to go directly to your favourite, you can search by title, director, lead actor or year of release. It's even possible to try before you buy with a fine selection of online trailers.

DVD Street **www.dvdstreet.co.uk**

The Streets folk earn another place in our hearts with this film-buff-friendly site. Searchable stock listings, short but sweet reviews and keen pricing make this a great place to look for both new releases and remastered classics. As the name suggests, the emphasis is on shiny discs rather than magnetic tape – but then video is *soooo* last century.

Blockbuster **www.blockbuster.co.uk**

On the high street, Blockbuster may be the video rental champion, but on the web it's more interested in selling you the latest releases. Both videos and DVDs are available – and if you still want to rent, there's a list of your nearest stores.

MovieTrak **www.movietrak.com**

If you can't justify buying a DVD, then Movietrak is more than happy to let you rent them online. Simply choose from its well-stocked range of titles and it will send you your DVD for seven days. Once you've finished with it, simply chuck it into the pre-paid envelope provided and send it back. It's a simple enough idea and it doesn't cost much more than renting from your local video shop. Sorry, Blockbuster, but someone beat you to it.

■ *The best of the rest*

BBC Shop **www.bbcshop.com**

From *This Life* to the *Tellytubbies*, you'll find something for all the family. Put us down for a Wallace and Gromit boxed set.

DVD World **www.dvdworld.co.uk**

The name is a bit of a giveaway. DVD players are available in addition to the shiny little fellas themselves, and there's plenty of background information for fans of the fast-growing format.

20 television

Couch potatoes rejoice! The internet is a telly addict's dream come true, offering constantly updated listings, background information on your favourite programmes, behind-the-scenes gossip and everything else you need to heighten your viewing pleasure.

News and listings

■ *The best of the best*

Digiguide www.digiguide.co.uk

No more scouring over a copy of the *TV Times* or squinting at Teletext to find out when your favourite programme's on. Digiguide is available both online and as a

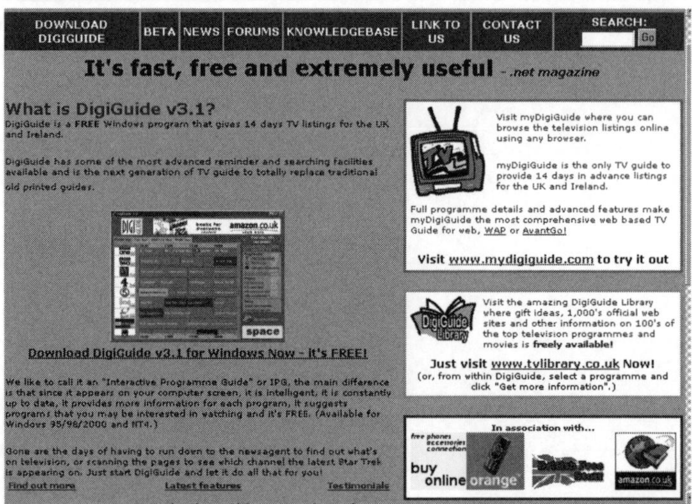

downloadable program that runs from Windows. Not only does it let you browse TV listings for the next couple of weeks, it's customised to your TV region and you can even ask it to alert you when a programme is about to start. If you have internet access at home, make sure you download the Digiguide program – it costs a few pounds a year but you'll wonder how you ever lived without it. A real gem.

■ *The rest of the best*

Unmissable TV **www.unmissabletv.com**

Unmissable TV offers a behind-the-scenes guide to your favourite programmes, suggestions of what to watch, celebrity features and, of course, a complete TV listings guide.

Teletext TV Plus **www.teletext.co.uk/tvplus**

Great news, everyone! You can now access Teletext without hunting for the remote control. The simple but uncluttered design makes it easy to check out what's on, and in-depth features provide more information about popular programmes than you could possibly need.

For more television news and information, check out Broadcasters and Programmes.

Broadcasters

■ *The best of the best*

BBC Online **www.bbc.co.uk**

You may not think that the BBC is the best broadcaster (especially if you're a sports fan), but on the web there really is nothing to touch it. With superb news and current affairs coverage, flawless educational material and quite possibly the best leisure and entertainment content you'll find anywhere, there's something for everyone – and there's even some TV-related information. How does it manage to be so good? Let's just say that a few million quid of licence money hasn't gone to waste.

The rest of the best

Carlton **www.carlton.co.uk**

Like the BBC, Carlton is using the web as much more than a promotional tool. Its main site features all the programme information you'd expect plus job, cinema, restaurant and property finders, competitions and corporate blurb, while for some of the best UK online leisure and entertainment, you'll definitely want to check out Jamba (**www.jamba.co.uk**), Popcorn (**www.popcorn.co.uk**) and Simply Food (**www.simplyfood.co.uk**).

Channel 4 **www.channel4.co.uk**

Suitably slick yet offbeat web presence from the UK's most innovative terrestrial channel. TV listings, background information and complete mini-sites for the most popular programmes make it well worth a look.

Channel 5 **www.channel5.co.uk**

Say what you like about Channel 5, it's certainly got a sense of fun. Right from the word go, you're bombarded with animation and excitement – with complete listings, chat, competitions and the slightly worrying 'Channel 5 Unleashed' to keep you entertained.

ITV **www.itv.co.uk**
ITV certainly has been busy, not just developing its main promotional presence but with the creation of loads of separate official sites dedicated to the channel's most popular programmes.

ONdigital **www.ondigital.co.uk**
There's certainly no shortage of movement on this guide to ON's digital offerings which provides information about the technology, the programmes, the stars and the sport – as well as trying to tempt you to sign up at every available opportunity.

Sky **www.sky.com**
Sky laughs in the face of TV guide sites with its complete information and entertainment portal. News, sport, current affairs, features, interviews, competitions, shopping and so much more – take a packed lunch, you'll be there for a while.

Programmes

The best of the best

TV Cream **www.tv.cream.org**
Relive your televisual childhood on this great site. From *Crackerjack* to *Cities of Gold* – it's all here.

The rest of the best

Baywatch	**www.baywatchtv.com**
BBC Comedy Zone	**www.comedyzone.beeb.com**
The Bill	**www.thebill.com**
Brookside	**www.brookie.com**
Coronation Street	**www.coronationstreet.co.uk**
EastEnders	**www.bbc.co.uk/eastenders**
Emmerdale	**www.emmerdale.co.uk**
Friends	**friends.warnerbros.com**
Friends Place	**www.friendsplace.com**
Hollyoaks	**www.hollyoaks.com**
Home and Away	**www.homeandaway.seven.com.au**
Ally McBeal	**www.allymcbeal.com**
Neighbours	**www.neighbours.com**
Pokémon	**www.pokemon.com**
Sesame Street	**www.sesamestreet.com**
South Park	**www.comedycentral.com/southpark**
Jerry Springer	**www.jerryspringer.com**
Star Trek	**www.startrek.com**
This Morning	**www.itv.thismorning.co.uk**
The X Files	**www.thexfiles.com**

21 live entertainment

Whether you're planning a night at the theatre or looking for tickets to a rock gig, you'll find plenty of online resources to make life that little bit easier.

Listings and ticket booking

■ *The best of the best*

What's On Stage **www.whatsonstage.com**
If theatre is your thing then What's On Stage should definitely be your first port of call. Not only does this massive performing arts resource provide an excellent guide to what's happening where – once you've chosen your performance you can view seating plans and even book tickets with the minimum of fuss.

■ *The rest of the best*

Aloud **www.aloud.com**

Simply type in the name of the artist, town or genre you're looking for and the booking engine will suggest possible events and dates. If you see something you like, it only takes a couple of clicks to make the booking. As with all ticket agents, you will pay a booking fee – but when ordering is as painless as this it's well worth the extra pennies.

Ticketmaster **www.ticketmaster.co.uk**

From athletics to the Farnborough Airshow and, of course, the UK's largest gigs, shows and concerts – whatever live events you want to be a part of, it only takes a couple of clicks to reserve your tickets. It doesn't get much better than this.

Ticketbank **www.ticketbank.co.uk**

It may not be the slickest ticket site on the web – in fact the online ordering facility looks positively naff – but, if you're looking for festival or gig tickets at competitive prices, Ticketbank is well worth a look.

■ *The best of the rest*

BBC Ticket Unit **www.bbc.co.uk/tickets**

Be in the studio audience for your favourite BBC shows. Just don't forget to applaud.

The Society of Ticket Agents & Resellers **www.s-t-a-r.org.uk**

If you can't find anywhere selling the tickets you want then it's worth trying STAR's list of members for some alternatives.

Useful information

■ *The best of the best*

The Stage **www.thestage.co.uk**

The Stage newspaper has been publishing news and information for the entertainment business since 1880, and although it's obviously an industry site,

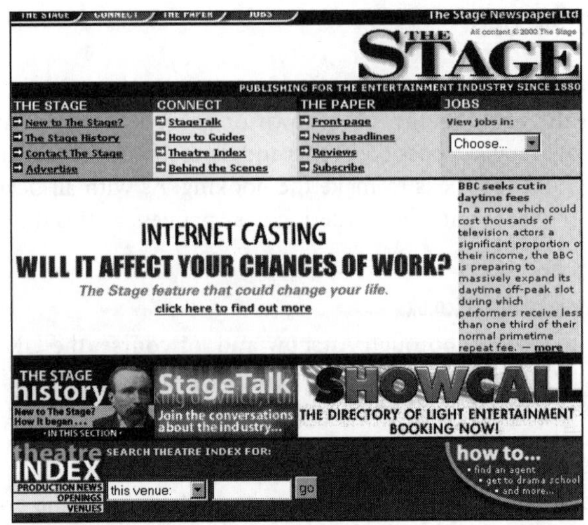

there's still plenty of useful stuff for non-luvvies, including a great directory of links to the best live entertainment resources on the web.

■ *The rest of the best*

The Royal Shakespeare Company **www.rsc.org.uk**

This official site contains full details of the RSC's productions in London, Stratford and across the UK as well as an interesting guide to the company's repertoire and plenty of educational information to keep teachers happy. Impressive stuff.

National Theatre Online **www.nt-online.com**

The National Theatre is famous for its first-class performances, so it seems only fitting that it should have an equally top-notch official site. All three theatres in the complex are covered and, if a particular production takes your fancy, you can book tickets online.

Ballet.co **www.ballet.co.uk**

This suitably elegant site contains a wealth of information about UK ballet, including the English National Ballet, the Royal Ballet and a selection of the country's other most popular companies.

Musical Stages www.musicalstages.co.uk

The magic of the musicals comes alive online through the official site of Britain's only musical theatre magazine.

Arts Books www.arts-books.com

Yes, it does sell books, but 'the store for performing arts' also offers a great range of music, videos, audio books and clothing covering ballet, ballroom, contemporary dance, opera, mime, drama and musical theatre.

The best of the rest

Really Useful Theatre www.reallyuseful.com

The official site of Andrew Lloyd Webber's theatre company includes plenty of information about *Starlight Express*, *Joseph* and all the other favourites.

UK Theatre Web www.uktw.co.uk

This very useful guide to the world of amateur and professional theatre in the UK also provides an impressive list of links to other relevant sites.

22 books, culture and the arts

The internet is a great way to make literature, poetry, museums, fashion and the arts accessible to a wide audience. Whether you're looking for the full text of *Paradise Lost* or the latest fashion gossip from the streets of Milan, it's all just a cultural click away.

Books and poetry

■ *The best of the best*

Books Unlimited **www.booksunlimited.co.uk**
Another great site from the *Guardian* stable, Books Unlimited offers reviews, author profiles, extracts from new titles and plenty of discussion and debate to keep things interesting. A real page-turner.

The rest of the best

The Good Book Guide **www.thegoodbookguide.com**

As its name suggests, this is an online guide to the latest book releases across a number of different genres. Updated weekly, the site has plenty to offer avid bookworms.

What Am I Going To Read? **www.whatamigoingtoread.com**

Can't decide what to read next? Take a look at WAIGTR for some great ideas, plus the opportunity to discuss new and popular titles with your fellow readers.

The Times Literary Supplement **www.the-tls.co.uk**

The *TLS* has been around since 1902 and, if its online edition is anything to go by, it has another few centuries in it yet. From Anthropology to Women's Studies, the excellent range of sections means there's something for everyone.

Project Gutenberg **www.gutenberg.org**

Project Gutenberg really has set itself a daunting task – to transfer every important literary text on to the internet. It seems to be doing pretty well – thousands of books have already been digitised and more are being added all the time, so check back often.

The British Library **www.bl.uk**

It may not be the easiest site in the world to browse, but the official online home of the British Library is an essential bookmark, with info on the library itself plus downloadable versions of classic books.

Poetry.com **www.poetry.com**

With a name like Poetry.com you'd expect something pretty special. Fortunately, the site doesn't disappoint, with a huge database of work by nearly 2 million poets and plenty of audio content for good measure.

About Poetry **www.poetry.about.com**

Want to know about poetry? You've come to the right place. This excellent human-edited guide to poetry resources on the web will keep you clicking for hours.

Museums and galleries

■ The best of the best

World Wide Arts Resources **www.world-arts-resources.com**

A well-written, comprehensive guide to the huge variety of online arts resources.

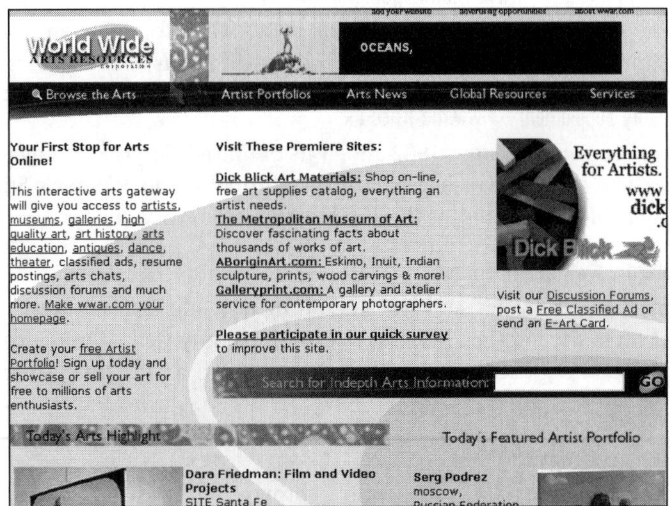

■ The rest of the best

24 Hour Museum **www.24hourmuseum.org.uk**

Gateway to over 2,000 major UK museums, galleries and historic buildings. Superb.

■ The best of the rest

The Louvre	**www.louvre.fr**	Guggenheim Museums	**www.guggenheim.org**
Georges Pompidou Centre	**www.cnac-gp.fr**	Smithsonian Institution	**www.mnh.si.edu**
The State Hermitage Museum	**www.hermitagemuseum.org**		

Fashion

The best of the best

Fashion Net **www.fashion.net**

Step into a world of fashion links and information for all the family, with this absolutely fabulous site.

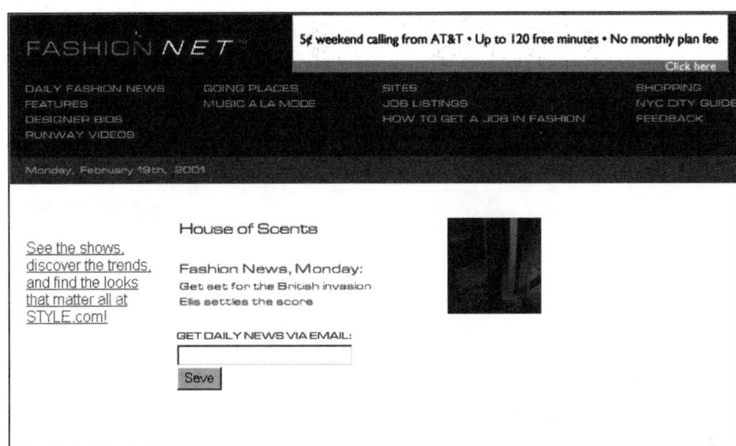

The best of the rest

f.uk **www.widemedia.com/fashionuk**

A nice-looking UK fashion site that knows exactly how cool it is. The f.uk joke is wearing a bit thin.

Lucire **www.lucire.com**

'The UK's global fashion magazine' takes a very well-turned-out look at the world of fashion, style and just plain coolness.

Elle Magazine **www.ellemag.com**

A glossy site from one of the world's most famous glossy magazines.

Book shopping

The best of the best

Book Brain www.bookbrain.co.uk

Bookbrain is one of those sites that make the internet worth using. The site doesn't actually sell any books itself, acting instead as a price comparison service for the big names in the business. Basically, you type in the name of the book you want and it will scour the most popular UK booksellers for the best price.

The rest of the best

BOL www.uk.bol.com

You can't fail to be impressed with a site offering over 1.5 million books at around 30 per cent off cover price. In addition to the shop itself, there are interviews with famous authors, plenty of gift ideas and some of the best book descriptions you'll find. Add in BOL's regular (and impressive) special offers and you have the recipe for retail heaven.

Waterstone's Online **www.waterstones.co.uk**

An impressive offering from the high street favourite. Waterstone's Online features the usual (huge) range of books and is also one of the first UK booksellers to offer downloadable electronic books.

Alphabet Street **www.alphabetstreet.co.uk**

Part of the Streets Online empire, Alphabet Street stocks a huge range of books at great prices. A firm favourite.

Online Originals **www.onlineoriginals.com**

Proving that not all bookshops are the same, Online Originals specialises in downloadable electronic versions of work from new authors. Fiction, non-fiction, drama and youth are all well represented, and the quality of writing is comparable with more traditional books.

■ *The best of the rest*

Basically Books **www.basicallybooks.co.uk**

Basically Books specialises in children's titles. The site is straightforward to browse and offers helpful plot summaries and a guide to which age groups each title is best suited.

Booklovers **www.booklovers.co.uk**

Booklovers specialises in tracking down second-hand and out-of-print books. The site is based around a very user-friendly search system – and if you can't find the title you're looking for, Booklovers will try its hardest to get it for you. Superb prices, and the site works like a dream. If you have no luck, try the Amazon-owned American alternative, Bibliofind (**www.bibliofind.com**).

Magazine Shop **www.magazineshop.co.uk**

Looking for magazines? Look no further than this great virtual newsagent.

23 sport

If you're looking for a general overview of the latest sporting action, you'll definitely want to head over to one of our recommended portals or information sites. Although every site has its own unique features and style, you'll usually find news headlines and results relating to recent games, team profiles, celebrity gossip, competitions and plenty of links to other more specialist sites.

UK sports news

■ *The best of the best*

Sportal www.sportal.co.uk

It's hard to fault the depth of coverage on the UK version of this huge European network of sports sites. Football, tennis, Formula 1, horseracing, rugby union, rugby

league, cycling and more are covered in excellent detail through well-written reports, live commentary, instantly updated stats and some great photography.

■ *The rest of the best*

Sports.com **www.sports.com**

With a name like Sports.com you would be forgiven for assuming that this is an American site when, in fact, it's one of the best places to find European sports news, results and gossip. The layout is slightly more cluttered than Sportal and there certainly doesn't seem to the same depth of content, but if you want to know what's going on from a European perspective without flitting from one site to another, this is a worthy starting point.

BBC Sport **news.bbc.co.uk/sport**

News, player profiles, audio and video highlights, discussion forums and up-to-the-minute results, all presented in an extremely easy-to-browse format, make this site a joy to use, but it's the extra touches which make the site so special.

Sporting Life **www.sporting-life.com**

It may be light on photography and flashy features but when it comes to sporting news, Sporting Life's coverage is hard to fault – and if you can't find what you're looking for there's even a news feed providing up-to-the-minute news from Reuters, Sportal and other major players.

Sky Sports **www.skysports.co.uk**

Not satisfied with snapping up the rights to just about every sports event in the UK, Sky Sports has put together an extremely well-thought-out internet presence to rival the BBC Sport site. The standard of news, as you would expect, is excellent, with photography and even video to provide a complete picture and, if you need more information, there's a round-up of top stories from the day's newspapers.

Global sports news

■ *The best of the best*

Sports News **www.sportsnews.com**

Sports News covers events from Australia to Zimbabwe, and everywhere in between. The mix of sports is impressive too, including athletics, baseball, basketball, boxing, climbing, cricket, cycling, football, golf, hockey and so much more – all covered in impressive detail with photography and a whole world of interactivity. Look out for a great links section.

■ *The rest of the best*

Yahoo! Sports **sports.yahoo.com**

Yahoo! Sports provides world sports headlines plus links to other relevant sites and resources, although there's a definite (unashamedly) American bias so don't expect a truly global view. For proper world sport click on the 'worldwide' button towards the top of the front page.

Quokka Sports Network **www.quokka.com**

If you have a fast connection (or endless patience) you'll love Quokka's blend of multimedia content and in-depth sporting analysis. Frighteningly thorough and impressively interactive.

ESPN **www.espn.com**

OK, so 'international' does seem to mean American, but such is the way of the web. Another Stateside attempt at world domination comes in the form of ESPN, one of the biggest sports broadcasters in the world and probably the best place to find information on the NHL, NBL and NFL. The site also owns a chunk of Soccernet (**www.soccernet.com**) – see Football for more information.

Oxygen Sports **www.wesweat.com**

Formerly known as 'We Sweat' (nice!), Oxygen Sports is an American news and information site aimed at modern independent women. Athletics, baseball, basketball, golf, ice hockey, running, soccer, tennis, triathlon, volleyball, water sports, weightlifting and wrestling are among the sports on offer, with live audio and video as well as top-quality writing to keep you up to date.

Nine MSN Sport **sports.ninemsn.com.au**

Just in case the MSN bit didn't give it away, this slick sports site is another tentacle of Microsoft's sprawling internet octopus – this time aimed at an Australian audience. All the usual sports are listed and it's very interesting to read about world sports events from an Aussie perspective – just remember that it's soccer, not football.

Football

■ *The best of the best*

Football 365 **www.football365.co.uk**

What started life as a daily e-mail newsletter has grown into a huge football megasite filled with the usual news and features plus discussion forums, competitions and some extremely sharp sports journalism. The emphasis is definitely on content over presentation and, although the site is easy enough to use,

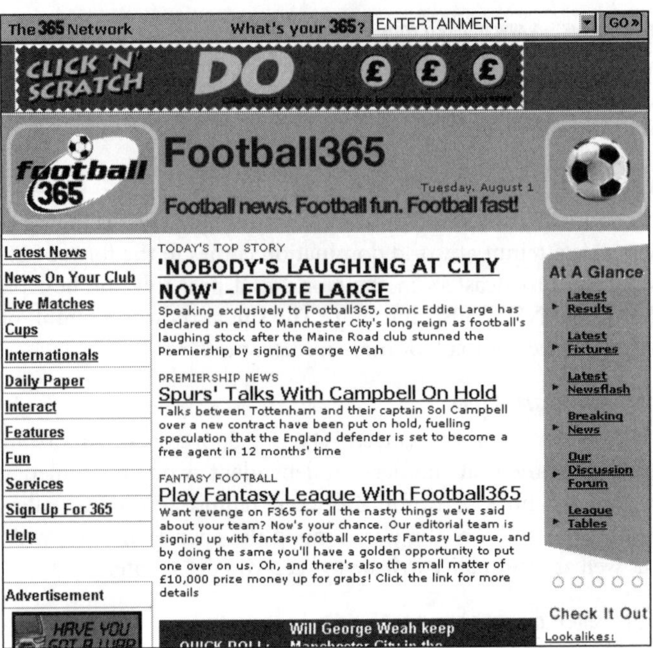

there are very few graphics – with massive amounts of text to make up for it. All in all, this may not be the glossiest site in the world – but if you love football, you'll love Football 365.

The rest of the best

Soccernet **www.soccernet.com**

This site has changed hands more often than a dodgy car stereo, having been sold originally by its 15-year-old founder to Associated Newspapers, which then sold it on to the American sports giant ESPN. The change of ownership doesn't seem to have had any adverse effects on the quality of the site, which is big on news and offers a dedicated page for every single League club in England and those in the top flight in Scotland. The site doesn't quite match the 'by the fans, for the fans' feel of Football 365, but if you want fast facts it's a great place to start.

Soccer Age **www.soccerage.com**

This is what global football coverage should be like – unbiased, multilingual, well-written and easy to browse. Whether you're following the English Premiership or the Italian Serie A, you'll find it all here, and plenty more besides.

Football FC **www.footballfc.co.uk**

The fact that Football FC has close links with the *Sun* means two things: firstly that it contains some of the best football stories on the web; and secondly, that the site uses any excuse to show pictures of scantily clad women.

Soccer Base **www.soccerbase.com**

This site's daily fixtures list and up-to-the-minute results make it well worth visiting – with enough data on players, transfers, managers and grounds to keep even the most dedicated stats fan occupied for weeks. Superb.

Planet Football **www.planetfootball.com**

A cluttered but comprehensive site specialising in combining news with official OPTA statistics to give a complete picture of UK and European football.

Rec.Sport.Soccer Statistics Foundation **www.rsssf.com**

Anyone who has been using the web since before 1997 will feel instantly at home on the RSSSF site. Glossy photos and innovative layout have been shunned in favour of good old-fashioned information overload, with statistics from pretty well every league in pretty well every European country.

Ladies Football **www.ladies-football.co.uk**

Not only does Ladies Football provide a thorough Ladies Football League directory, containing links to websites for clubs throughout Great Britain, but there's also a forum, chat and direct links to similar directories for school and Sunday league teams.

For a host of links to major UK and international football sites, check out Football Pages (**www.footballpages.com**), Soccer Links (**www.soccerlinks.com**) and, of course, the Zingin Football Guide (**www.zingin.com/guide/leisure/sport/football**).

Rugby

■ *The best of the best*

Planet Rugby **www.planet-rugby.com**

Planet Rugby offers everything a rugby fan could possibly want, including the latest news and match reports, international fixtures, photo gallery, statistics, discussion boards and the ever popular rugby lookalikes (you have to see it).

■ *The rest of the best*

Scrum **www.scrum.com**

A great name for a great site – Scrum complements the usual portal fodder with a wealth of innovative features which do an excellent job of covering every possible aspect of the sport. If you're new to the game, you'll find a handy rugby primer to get you started, while old hands will love the live chats with top players and the chance to buy posters and other bits and pieces in the shopping section.

Rugby **www.rugby.com**

As well as having the presence of mind and good fortune to register the name Rugby.com before anyone else, this uncluttered international round-up is impressive to say the least. There may not be a raft of extra features – you'll want to visit Scrum for that – but the quality of reporting and depth of coverage are more than enough to make up for the lack of gimmicks. Well worth a visit.

World of Rugby **www.worldofrugby.com**

There's a whole world of rugby out there – and most of it is covered here. From Asia to Wales, you'll find a wealth of up-to-the-minute rugby news, presented in a well-written but not particularly gripping way.

World of Rugby League **www.rleague.com**

True to its name, the site covers matches and teams from around the world, with the Australian NRL rubbing e-shoulders with our very own Tetley Super League – and, while there is something of a lack of polish, you can't fault its no-frills, easy-to-browse format.

About Rugby **rugby.about.com**

About specialises in providing expert guides to different aspects of the internet, with links, forums and advice to help you find what you're looking for. Its rugby section, as with the rest of the service, doesn't fail to impress, with a good selection of the best websites, resources and e-zines to keep you surfing well into the early hours. Great stuff.

Check the progress of your favourite national team by visiting one of the many official and unofficial fan sites listed in the Zingin Rugby Guide (**www.zingin.com/guide/leisure/sport/rugby**).

Cricket

■ *The best of the best*

CricInfo **www.cricinfo.com**

CricInfo is without doubt the finest cricket site on the web. Having picked up

numerous awards for its depth of coverage, which borders on the obsessive at times, the site continues to go from strength to strength with news, statistics, chat and, most impressive of all, a live scoreboard which provides up-to-the-second match coverage so you'll never miss a wicket, no matter where in the world you happen to be.

■ *The rest of the best*

Wisden **www.wisden.com**

CricInfo may be all things to all cricket fans but it's hard to compete with the experience that comes from over 135 years of continuous publishing – and with a ton of online match reports, detailed statistics and enthralling articles, Wisden's future seems pretty secure. Irreverent it ain't – fascinating reading it most certainly is.

Goldwire Cricket **www.goldwirecricket.com**

Strange name, great site. Goldwire looks deceptively bland when you first arrive, but beneath the distinctively unflashy interface lies a wealth of match reports and scores.

Lords **www.lords.org**

The official site of the home of cricket may take itself a little too seriously, but you can't fault its reporting of the latest cricket news, complete with up-to-the-minute score information and some nifty audio content to keep your ears happy.

Tennis

■ *The best of the best*

Tennis Org UK **www.tennis.org.uk**

Although it doesn't seem to have been updated for a while, Tennis Org is a great directory of tennis-related websites, resources and other information. If you're not exactly sure what you're looking for, you can browse the directory by categories which include health, shopping, news and techniques or simply type in keywords, click the 'Serve Now!' button and see what comes up. It may not look great, but it works well and there's nothing else like it.

The rest of the best

Lawn Tennis Association **www.lta.org.uk**

Impressive site from the British Lawn Tennis Association with a definite emphasis on getting young people involved in the game.

Wimbledon **www.wimbledon.org**

OK, maybe the chances of reaching Wimbledon are a little slim for most of us, but if you visit this superb official site during the tournament you'll be treated to constantly updated scores, player profiles, match photos and even a weather forecast to check whether rain is likely to stop play. Ace.

The International Tennis Federation **www.itftennis.com**

Tennis is one of the few sports which can rightly claim global popularity – that's the message from the official ITF website which is packed full of international competition news, from the Davis Cup to the Olympics, along with a guide to the rules, some useful facts and figures and plenty of photos of tennis superstars.

Real Tennis **www.real-tennis.com**

Forget fake tennis – this is the real deal. In case you weren't sure, real tennis was the forerunner of lawn tennis (as played at Wimbledon) and is not dissimilar to the game we usually play today – except that the court has walls which the ball is allowed to bounce off. OK, so it's a little more complex than that but the rules are explained extremely well here, with diagrams and photographs to illustrate the slightly strange court set-up. If you're bored with normal tennis, maybe it's time to get real.

The Tennis Server **www.tennisserver.com**

Ho ho ho, how they must have chuckled when they thought up the name Tennis Server (it's a pun – you see?), although perhaps calling it the 'Center Court for Tennis on the Internet' is pushing our pun tolerance a little far. Naffness aside, this American site features a huge number of articles for both fans and budding players alike, along with some of the most useful tennis coaching advice on the net (sorry, almost another pun there) and even makes a fair attempt at covering non-US competitions.

Squash

■ *The best of the best*

Internet Squash Federation **www.squash.org**

If it's squash-related, it's almost certainly going to be on this excellent resource. The grandly titled Internet Squash Federation has a massive site filled with news, results, features, rules, rankings, clubs, comment and an international round-up of tournaments and players. Obviously, when there are so few squash sites, being the best of the best doesn't mean much – but even if there were a million other options, it's unlikely that many would come this close to perfection. Splendid.

■ *The rest of the best*

Squash Player **www.squashplayer.co.uk**

The layout leaves a little to be desired but you can't fault the content of Squash Player, which is filled with news on how British players are getting on around the world, a definitive guide to the UK game and plenty of the classic award ceremony photography beloved by special-interest publications.

US Squash **www.us-squash.org**

Bit self-explanatory this one. It's a site about squash in the US. Act surprised.

Badminton and table tennis

■ *The best of the best*

The European Table Tennis Union **www.ettu.org**

We thought that the International Badminton Federation had a grand sounding name until we encountered the European Table Tennis Union. This surprisingly impressive site contains a satisfying blend of news, rankings, results and somewhat comedic action shots – all wrapped up in a very slick design which would put many of the much larger sports sites to shame.

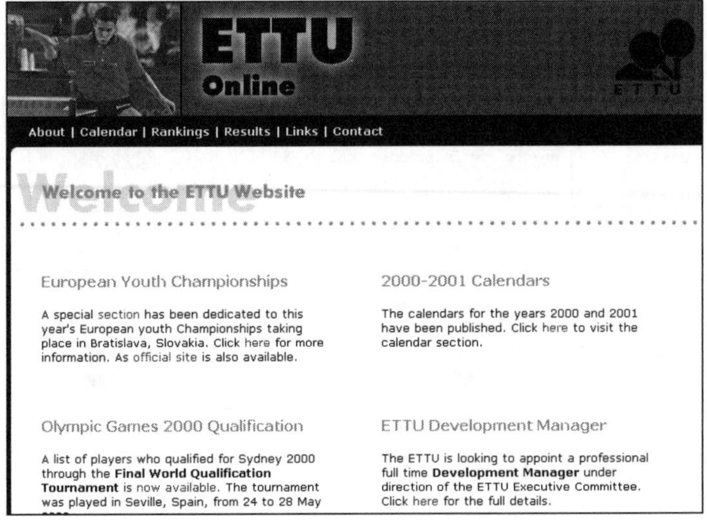

■ *The rest of the best*

Badminton UK **www.badmintonuk.ndo.co.uk**

This unofficial site is maintained by a UK badminton enthusiast and, considering it's a one-man show, it's all very impressive. There's not a great deal on offer for fans – but players will find a massive amount of useful information, including a directory of clubs and associations, a thriving message board and one of the most complete lists of links you'll find. A superb effort.

International Badminton Online **www.intbadfed.org**

If slow-motion tennis is your thing, you'll definitely want to head over to the official site of the sport's governing body. No fancy graphics or live video here – just news, rules and a happy, smiling bee-type mascot thing.

Track and field

■ *The best of the best*

Asimba **www.asimba.com**

Asimba is a fitness site for those of us who are a little too fond of pies and not fond enough of running 26 miles without stopping. The idea is to get you into shape not just through running but also by changing your diet, training properly, swimming, cycling and generally watching less TV.

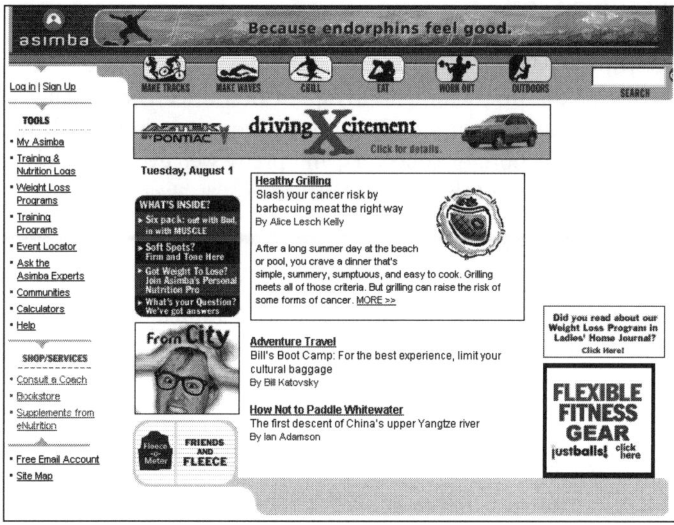

The rest of the best

Athletics Online **www.athletics-online.co.uk**

Results, news, messages, chat and links make this a great place to go for UK athletics information.

International Amateur Athletics Federation **www.iaaf.org**

The name of the game here is news, news and even more news from the worldwide governing body of amateur athletics. If, heaven forbid, you should tire of the news then make sure you check out the multimedia gallery featuring IAAF members in action and the downloadable handbook to ensure that you stay on track (pun intended). The organisation may be for amateurs, but the site is absolutely professional in every way.

UK Running Track Directory **www.runtrackdir.com**

An impressively complete listing of UK tracks, searchable by location and surface type, plus a directory of links to athletic clubs across the UK. It does exactly what it says on the tin.

The best of the rest

Olympics **www.olympics.org**

The official site of the International Olympic Committee is a suitably slick affair, complete with an online Olympic museum, information about both the summer and winter games, a section for collectors, and pretty well everything else you could possibly need to know about the world's favourite sports event.

uk:athletics **www.ukathletics.org**

You know a site is trying to be cool when it uses lower-case letters for its name – and uk:athletics is no exception. The official site of the 'National Governing Body for the sport of athletics in the UK' is certainly impressive, with an events diary, results, records, biographies and the slightly sparse lifestyle section which tries to persuade you to get into a pair of Lycra shorts.

Runner's World **www.runnersworld.com**

The spin-off site from the magazine of the same name is full of straight-talking news and reviews, plus all of the information serious runners require to compete. An excellent resource, not for the faint-hearted.

Runner's Web **www.runnersweb.com**

A wonderfully cluttered American site designed by fans for fans (aren't they all?), Runner's Web contains a headache-inducing number of features, including an interactive calendar, forums, regular articles and over 40 other useful sections to keep you clicking away for hours.

Gymnastics

■ *The best of the best*

BAGA **www.baga.co.uk**

Remember BAGA awards at school? The sporty kids with their little sew-on badges for achieving 50 cartwheels and a forward roll, and the less flexible kids looking on with a mixture of envy and apathy – oh, happy days! The British Gymnastics Association is responsible for controlling the sport in the UK – and its official site is well worth a visit for gymnasts and spectators alike. The latest news, results and

future Olympic hopefuls are all present and correct – with a useful collection of links to clubs across the UK.

■ *The rest of the best*

Gymnastics Forum **www.gymn-forum.com**

Gymnast profiles, news, an e-mail newsletter and other bits and pieces are all extremely well-written, but the presentation is a little bland at times and, considering the popularity of the site, you'd expect a bit more. Look out for the 'n' in 'gymn' when you're typing this one in.

Gym World **www.gymworld.com**

A true community site, Gym World offers gymnasts the chance to meet, discuss, swap tips and bitch about their rivals. There's plenty to see and do, but one of the best bits is the little animated character who performs various springy moves which can then be discussed by visitors to the site. When we last visited she was having problems with her landing – not bending her legs enough, apparently.

International Gymnast **www.intlgymnast.com**

Making an effortless double back flip from a paper to the web, International Gymnast contains everything you'd expect from the popular magazine plus an archive of past articles, a photo gallery, a section for kids, a monthly poll and plenty more.

Sailing and canoeing

■ *The best of the best*

Yacht and Boating World **www.ybw.co.uk**

Europe's largest marine portal (boat site to the rest of us) offers information from such highly respected titles as *Yachting World*, *Yachting Monthly* and *Motorboat and Yachting,* as well as a continuously updated run-down of the latest nautical news and a well-stocked sailing shop.

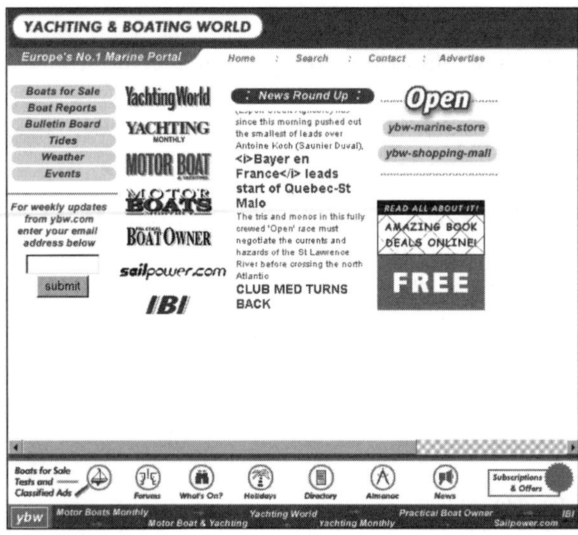

The rest of the best

Yachts and Yachting **www.intersail.co.uk**

Club listings, a calendar, photography, coaching tips, weather and tides, and classified adverts are all easily accessible from a straightforward navigation system, and there's a real sense of community created by the fact that yacht enthusiasts can submit their own regatta reports and results for publication online.

ePaddler **www.epaddler.com**

If you're into canoeing or kayaking you simply must bookmark this top-notch site. It may be based in the US but, unlike many of the other Stateside sites, it clearly realises that there's a whole world of canoeing out there. Look out for the frighteningly complete list of links.

Yacht **www.yacht.co.uk**

No cluttered menus and text-filled front page here – just easy-to-navigate, well-written information for both beginners and experts. There's plenty to see, but our favourite features are the sailing club listings and links to the best of the watery web. For an international viewpoint, check out The Sailing Source (**www.paw.com/saw**).

Royal Yachting Association **www.rya.org.uk**

A whole world of sailing information to whet your appetite, from the whereabouts of your local club to training schools, news, events and even a suitably gripping account of RYA council meetings. Nifty menu system, too.

Paddling.net **www.paddling.net**

If it's canoeing and kayaking info you're after, you've come to the right place. This US-oriented site contains product reviews, a directory of outfitters, message boards and loads of extra goodies. The only minor problem is that most of the events and products mentioned are only for folks on the other side of the Atlantic. Oh well.

Swimming

■ *The best of the best*

Swim Rating **www.swimrating.com**

If you're serious about your swimming, as most swimmers are, you'll love Swim Rating. The concept is simple. You enter your personal best times for any distance and the site adds and divides in order to calculate your swim rating. Once you have

a rating you can then, in the great swimmers' tradition, compare it with those of the huge numbers of other people who use the site. Addictive and competitive – bit like swimming really.

■ *The rest of the best*

Swimnet **www.swimnet.co.uk**

Swimnet seems to be all about getting people involved in the sport by making it easy to find your local pool while dazzling you with video footage of top stars in action. The layout is not particularly inspiring in itself, but if you enjoy swimming or fancy giving it a try, you'll find everything you need to get motivated and get involved. We like.

Sub Aqua Association **www.saa.org.uk**

If swimming underwater is more your style, the Sub Aqua Association site contains everything you need to start diving. There's an impressive amount of diving news on offer plus discussion forums to swap tricks and tips with your fellow sub-aqua enthusiasts.

FINA **www.fina.org**

Make sure you're playing by the rules by paying a quick visit to the official site of swimming's governing body.

Surfing, windsurfing and water-skiing

■ *The best of the best*

Cold Swell **www.coldswell.com**

If you're planning on catching some waves in the UK then you'll definitely want to check out Cold Swell's up-to-the-minute surf forecasts and satellite photos before you go; if desktop surfing is more your style, the comprehensive links directory will keep your mouse busy for hours.

■ *The rest of the best*

Surfcall **www.surfcall.co.uk**

Surfcall has been providing accurate surf reports for over a decade and is now taking advantage of the internet by offering a live webcam view of UK beaches, allowing you to avoid a wasted trip or just watch the rolling waves from the comfort of your desk. Nice.

Wavecam **www.wavecam.com**

For a whole world of webcams look no further than Wavecam, which offers live cams, pre-recorded video and stunning photography of the planet's most popular surf spots.

British and European Waterskiing **www.waterski-uk.com**

'The home of British waterskiing in cyberspace' is a little sparse in design but makes up for it with some thoroughly entertaining content, including a club listing, history of the sport, forum, wakeboarding and kneeboarding stuff, and even a caption competition. For a more official water-skiing resource, jump over to British Water Ski Online (**www.bwsf.co.uk**).

Association of Surfing Professionals **www.aspeurope.com**

Only those who take their surfing seriously are welcome on this impressive looking but slightly disjointed site. Apparently the association looks after the interests of professional surfers at a local level and, with offices around the world, it's certainly a force to be reckoned with.

Waterski A-Z   www.waterski-az.co.uk

If you're looking for words – look no further, there are plenty here. Clickable news headlines, tips and tricks, a forum and even a ski shop are cunningly hidden behind one of the most confusing layouts we've ever seen.

Boards Online   www.boards.co.uk

Tons of information, much of which is taken from the site's off-line version. Boards – plus news, weather and even videos of people riding waves, falling off them and generally splashing about. Check out Boards and you certainly won't be. Bored, that is.

Skiing and snowboarding

■ *The best of the best*

1Ski   www.1ski.co.uk

Whether you're looking for your nearest dry slope or a fortnight in the Alps, there's something for you in this excellent resource, which offers travel booking, advice on

skiing technique, stunning photography, getting a job in the snow and pretty much everything else you need to go on the piste.

■ *The rest of the best*

Board It **www.boardit.com**

Your one-stop shop for all things snowboardy. Make travel arrangements, find out the latest snowboarding news, browse the photo galleries and even check out a webcam for your chosen resort. One of our favourite features is the tip of the day: 'get off the hill by around three p.m. because there are many other tired people out there and you don't want to meet them via collision'. Quite right.

Ski Pages **www.skipages.com**

Don't even think about going skiing until you've checked out Ski Pages. The easy-to-browse directory of over 500 ski resorts, the guide to nearly 600 ski and snowboard resorts around the world, the news, the auctions and the people wrapped up in warm clothing. Does life get any better than this? (Sigh.)

Complete Skier **www.complete-skier.com**

What this nifty site lacks in slick design and action photography it more than makes up for in content, with all of the news, travel info, tips, tricks and features you need to hit the slopes – and it's British, too. Nice work.

Snowboarding UK **www.snowboardinguk.co.uk**

No misplaced gloss or glamour, no bull – just one of the finest winter sports directories and links sites on the web. For a Stateside slant, check out Snowboarding.com (**www.snowboarding.com**).

■ *The best of the rest*

Ski.co.uk **www.ski.co.uk**

Not quite as glossy as the likes of 1Ski and Ski Pages but nonetheless a great way to keep up to date with all things relating to skiing in the UK.

Snowboarding Online **www.snowboarding-online.com**

Funky, feature-packed American site for snowboarders around the world.

Other winter sports

■ *The best of the best*

Ice Hockey UK **www.icehockeyuk.co.uk**

The official site of Ice Hockey UK provides details of how the organisation is looking after the interests of hockey players and also features club news, links, press releases and a premium-rate helpline. Definitely one for the players rather than the fans.

Euro Hockey **www.eurohockey.net**

As the name suggests, Euro Hockey is dedicated to providing information on the sport for people living on this side of the Atlantic. At the time of writing it wasn't quite up to speed, but the site is planning to have schedules, scores and standings from all European nations. Impressive stuff.

FIBT **www.fibt.com**

The International Bobsleigh and Tobogganing Federation (ignore the initials above, it's French!) is the governing body for people who like to sit in sledges and hurtle down very slippery slopes. The site is heavy on news and light on design, but will prove fascinating to anyone involved in the sport.

National Ice Skating Association **www.iceskating.org.uk**

Another official site, this time for budding Torvill and Deans. Like most governing body sites, there's a whole load of news, fixtures and contact details but not a great deal for the fans. It's difficult to complain though, as it does what it's supposed to – and does it well.

The English Ice Hockey Association **www.eiha.co.uk**

The English Ice Hockey Association has administered ice hockey in England since 1983, and its experience is certainly evident on this superb site. There are separate sections dealing with the men's, women's and youth game, plus regularly updated association news so you can keep up with what's going on in the sport.

The A to Z of Ice Hockey **www.azhockey.com**

If you've tried the above sites and drawn a blank, you'll definitely want to consult this huge list of ice hockey links. Sites and resources from around the world are listed and, for a refreshing change, the site is based in the UK.

Motor sports

■ *The best of the best*

ITV F1 **www.itv-f1.com**

ITV and Formula 1 are pretty closely connected, so it's not surprising that their F1 site is the best in the business. There's the usual mix of news, results and features, but it's the extra in-depth information that really makes the site stand out. The profiles of drivers and teams, photography, delivery of results to your mobile phone and the top-notch newsletter make for an excellent combination and any Formula 1 fan worth their salt will want to check it out now.

■ *The rest of the best*

Formula1.com **www.formula1.com**

Another strong contender for the finest Formula 1 site on the web, providing up-to-the-minute news, timing, features, gossip and rumour, online betting and plenty of pictures of very fast cars. Formula1.com may not be officially affiliated with Bernie

Ecclestone and friends – but if you want to find out the latest, there really is only one place to come.

Planet F1 www.planet-f1.com

Bringing you the power, the pressure and the passion of Formula 1 racing is the mission of this slick unofficial site. The formula (no pun intended) is the same as usual – news, results and so forth – but the presentation is particularly impressive, with an extremely busy but well-ordered front page providing direct access to a huge number of features.

Rally Zone www.rallyzone.co.uk

When you first arrive at Rally Zone you'd be forgiven for thinking there isn't much to it – a simple menu on the left and a what's new section to the right, and that's about it. But you can't judge a site by its front page – and if you dig below the surface you'll find an absolutely superb set of features which go well beyond the usual news, photos and results combo so beloved by other sports sites.

F1 Today **www.f1today.com**

Looking for yesterday's Formula 1 action? It looks like you're out of luck. F1 Today is a clutter-free source of the latest F1 news, all sorted into neat little bundles to make browsing straightforward. If you're looking for dramatic photography and full-motion video, you'll need to check out ITV F1 – but if short, sharp, reliable reporting is the important thing, this is a pretty safe bet.

World Rally **www.worldrally.net**

Probably the most maroon sports site on the web. World Rally provides race results from every rallying country you can think of – all bang up to date and as accurate as you could possibly want.

■ *The best of the rest*

Support your favourite team by visiting some of these all-singing, all-dancing official sites.

Jordan	**www.jordangp.com**	Williams	**www.williamsf1.co.uk**
McLaren	**www.mclaren.co.uk**		

Motorcycles

■ *The best of the best*

Bike Links **www.dropbears.com/bikelinks**

From buying and insuring a bike through to racing tips and results, this site offers bike-related links for every occasion. If you like the smell of burning rubber and enjoy wearing leather this could well be your idea of heaven.

■ *The rest of the best*

Speed-Way **www.speed-way.com**

The name says it all, really – this no-frills site contains a massive amount of information and features for the speedway enthusiast. News, fixtures, results, discussion groups, opinion and a fan club listing are among the goodies on offer.

The Superbike World Championship **www.superbike.it**

The official site of the Superbike World Championship is a suitably slick and feature-packed affair – even if it is a little cluttered. Contains everything you could possibly want to know about the competition itself as well as behind-the-scenes gossip, a webcam, links and some extremely exciting photography which will impress even those who aren't bike fans.

British Superbikes **www.british-superbikes.co.uk**

It may contain a little too much text for our tastes, but you can't fault the depth of information packed into this slightly irreverent superbike news site. As well as the latest info and results, make sure you take a look at some of the well-chosen links.

Equestrian sports

■ *The best of the best*

British Horseracing Board **www.bhb.co.uk**

An invaluable resource for both jockeys and fans, the official British Horseracing Board site looks great, is packed to the rafters with information and works like a

dream. There's information about the board – who they are, what they do, what they don't do, etc. – plus a daily guide to which races are happening where and when, news straight from the horse's mouth (sorry) and information about the BHB's campaigns to protect the interests of people involved in the industry. A clear favourite.

■ *The rest of the best*

The British Horse Society **www.bhs.org.uk**

Every conceivable facet of horses and riding seems to be covered here, from riding clubs to clipart via hunting discussions and online accident reporting. You'll have to trot over here to believe how much is on offer. For more of the same, check out the Jockey Club (**www.jockeyclub.com**).

British Dressage **www.britishdressage.co.uk**

The newly revamped British Dressage site is every bit as well groomed as the horses themselves although, at the time of writing, not all of the features were online. If you prefer a more genteel alternative to horseracing, this could well be right up your street.

The best of the rest

Aintree	**www.aintree.co.uk**	Chepstow	**www.chepstow.co.uk**
Ascot	**www.ascot.co.uk**	Goodwood	**www.goodwood.co.uk**
Cheltenham	**www.cheltenham.co.uk**		

Boxing

The best of the best

World Boxing **www.world-boxing.com**

While other sports sites have to rely on fans to provide the features, World Boxing has recruited some of the real heavyweights (pun intended) in the business, including Frank Warren, Barry McGuigan and John Dillon, who are all happy to share their experience and opinion with the site's huge user base. Excellent.

The rest of the best

Heavyweights **www.heavyweights.co.uk**

Tyson, Lewis, Holyfield and the rest of the big boys of boxing are the subject of this impressive site dedicated to providing news from the heavyweight division. Well-written features, results, pictures of people getting punched very hard and links – what more could you ask? A gum shield perhaps.

World Boxing Association **www.wbaonline.com**

The official site of the WBA is an essential bookmark for budding fighters and fans alike. After preaching the importance of uniformity, cooperation and control, the site goes on to report the latest match news, rankings and event information, complete with reproductions of all the official documents relating to WBA business. Well worth a look.

Fight News **www.fightnews.com**

If boxing news is worth knowing then you'll find it here. Up-to-the-minute reports, match reviews and an archive of results for the last few years, plus some useful links to other news sites and governing bodies.

Boxing Monthly **www.boxing-monthly.co.uk**

The electronic version of the popular monthly boxing magazine features a complete list of contents from the current issue, selected features and, of course, information on how to subscribe.

Wrestling

■ *The best of the best*

About Amateur Wrestling **amateurwrestle.about.com**

About.com does it again with this extremely useful guide to the world of amateur wrestling. As you might expect from a directory site, the emphasis is on links to wrestling resources elsewhere on the web, but there are a fair number of great features to keep you busy before you go. An excellent site with a pleasing lack of the 'sports entertainment' crowd.

■ *The rest of the best*

WWF **www.wwf.com**

Speaking of sports entertainment, the WWF is the undisputed king of the ring

when it comes to big American actors shouting at each other. All of the stars, the matches, the pay-per-view advertising and the scantily clad women are here for your entertainment. You know the drill – wrestlers start fighting, there's a sudden appearance by an unexpected opponent, the bad guys lose, the good guys win. God bless America. For more of the same, check out WCW (**www.wcw.com**).

1Wrestling **www.1wrestling.com**

Pro wrestling's daily news source provides a whole world of fight information, with a definite emphasis on the less real side of the 'sport'. If The Rock, The Undertaker and the rest of the gang are your scene, you'll lap this up. For more pro wrestling news, check out PWBTS (**www.pwbts.com**).

Martial arts

■ *The best of the best*

Judo World **www.judoworld.com**

Judo may not have as many movies based on it (*Judo Kid*?) but it's still an incredibly popular martial art around the world. Judo World attempts to bring together global

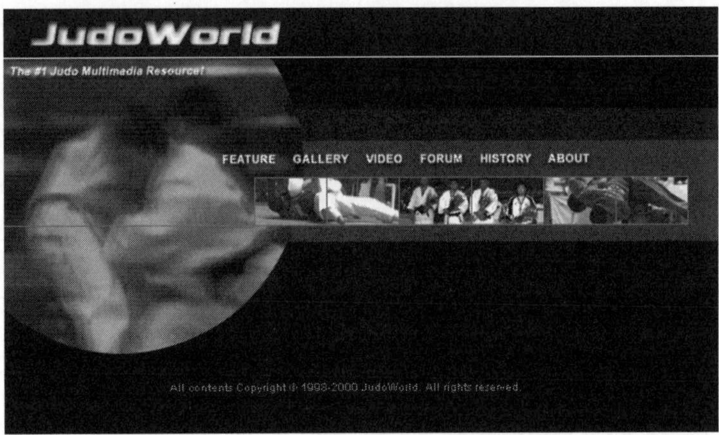

information about the sport with regularly updated tournament dates and reviews, interviews and even video clips so you can see how the experts do it.

The rest of the best

National Register of Martial Arts Instructors **www.nrmai.co.uk**

There are some extremely useful features here, including excellent advice for students and information about child abuse which should be required reading for everyone involved in the teaching and practice of martial arts. On a lighter note, the site is also a great way to find out who not to pick a fight with in the pub.

British Council for Chinese Martial Arts **www.bccma.org.uk**

Tons of information about the Council itself, plus profiles of the different arts, news, an events calendar and even a screen saver allowing you to use your computer to prove how tough you are.

Bushido Online **www.bushido.ch**

All of the karate, kung fu, judo and wrestling information you could ever possibly need is packed into this professional-looking site. If you're serious about your sport then you won't be disappointed with the level of expertise evident on Bushido Online, while if you're new to the martial arts you won't feel out of your depth as the level is set just about right for any level of experience.

International TaeKwon-Do Association **www.itatkd.com**

Tae kwon do is one of the more impressive (and potentially painful) of the martial arts, and this impressive site provides plenty of information about the history, the Association, as well as in-depth training advice.

Martial Info **www.martialinfo.com**

If you still haven't found the information you need, then you're bound to have more luck on Martial Info. This American directory and information site provides a wealth of features and news, but its real strength is the huge listing of local and international martial arts sites. For even more of the same, check out Black Belt Search (**www.blackbeltsearch.com**).

Cycling

■ *The best of the best*

Bike Magic **www.bikemagic.com**

Bike Magic is all about the enjoyment of cycling and everything it involves. From well-written and thoroughly enjoyable features to almost evangelical articles on the

wonders of pedal power, this online magazine has enough reading material to keep you off the roads for days.

■ *The rest of the best*

Bike Zone **www.bikezone.com**

Bike Zone is like Bike Magic but with an American accent. Divided into zones, the site features a news zone, a gear zone, a finder zone (?), an info zone and a personalised 'my zone' – all of which contain an excellent range of features and articles for the dedicated peddler.

Tour de France **www.latour.fr**

This official, multilingual site covers every aspect of the world-famous cycle race. The results, the competitors and the course are all profiled in impressive detail – and if you happen to drop by during the competition itself, you'll find a complete stage-by-stage account of the action. *Très bon*.

Road Cycling **www.roadcycling.com**

The main feature here is the news and results section, which will keep you up to date with competitions around the world – while the in-depth training guides are full of suggested routes for dedicated cyclists, regardless of skill level. So what are you waiting for? Don your best yellow jersey and start peddling.

Golf

■ *The best of the best*

Golf Today **www.golftoday.co.uk**

Claiming to be 'Europe's premier online golf magazine', Golf Today has no shortage of features for the professional or part-time golfer. An events guide, competitions, discussion groups, mailing list and a veritable bunker full of articles make up over 9,000 pages of golfing goodies.

The rest of the best

Golf Online **www.golfonline.com**

Despite an obvious US slant, there's plenty of information here for golf fans across the globe, with in-depth coverage of major international competitions, player profiles, statistics, a run-down of the rules of the game and some first-rate action photography. Also, unlike some of the other golf megasites, there is a decent level of reporting on the women's game – so much so, in fact, that it's probably the best women's golf site on the web.

Golf Courses **www.golfcourses.org**

Reading about golf is all well and good, but what if you want to get out on the fairway yourself? Golf Courses provides, unsurprisingly, a guide to the UK's finest courses, complete with information about each venue, a well-written review, information about green fees and everything else you need to make an informed choice. Top hole.

Golf Links **www.golflinks.co.uk**

No matter what type of information you're looking for, a quick visit to this no-frills, information-packed site will have you well on your way towards the best golfing resources the internet has to offer. Bookmark it now.

Fishing

■ *The best of the best*

Fishing **www.fishing.co.uk**

'Europe's largest internet angling magazine' screams the front page, which is not the greatest of boasts when you consider how little competition it has for the title, but that minor quibble doesn't detract from the superb quality of the site. News, tips, tricks, bait, articles, links, product reviews, magazines, photo galleries, trophies, competitions, clubroom, classifieds, books, statistics, records ... the list goes on and on and on and on. We love it.

■ *The rest of the best*

Where to Fish **www.where-to-fish.com**

Looking for a change of scenery? Caught all there is to catch in your local river? Then you need Where to Fish, which will tell you exactly that in England, Scotland, Wales, Northern Ireland, the Republic of Ireland and even further afield.

Worldwide Angler **www.worldwideangler.com**

For a worldwide angle (sorry) on all things fishy make sure you check out this slick US-based but globally reaching site. The articles may be a little too American, but no matter where you're based you'll make good use of the online calculators to help you sum up your catch, the message boards to keep in touch with fishing friends across the globe, and not forgetting the angling postcards to share the fun with your friends and family.

The Internet Angling Club **www.fish-on-line.net**

The Internet Angling Club is your opportunity to 'talk fishing' with other anglers around the world. With a choice of six mailing lists you're bound to find people who share your particular fishing passion and, as it's absolutely free, it's well worth a look.

Anglers Net **www.anglersnet.co.uk**

Another great UK angling site, this time dealing with the basics of the sport from arranging licences to ensuring that you have the best equipment for the job.

Snooker and darts

■ *The best of the best*

Snooker Net **www.snookernet.com**

Up-to-the-minute news, a local club finder, the history of the game, a diary, the latest rankings, multimedia and more links than you can shake a cue at ensure that, on the web at least, snooker will remain popular for many years to come.

The rest of the best

Game On **www.embassydarts.com**

News, match reports, official rankings and lots more arrow-related bits and pieces make this a great first stop for darts info online – although we couldn't help but spot a marked absence of references to alcohol. Something's definitely amiss there. For pots more fun, check out Embassy Snooker (**www.embassysnooker.com**).

Cyberdarts **www.cyberdarts.com**

Cyberdarts may lack the polish (and budget) of the likes of Game On, but there's no shortage of information to be found. Rules, tournament reports, news, a directory of pubs (at last!) and some irreverent features make this a thoroughly enjoyable, non-corporate effort. For more of the same, check out Dart Base (**www.dartbase.com**).

Bull's Eye News Magazine **www.bullsinet.com**

With its coverage of 'the global darting scene', the veritable feast of news, articles and unadulterated darty talk that is Bull's Eye, certainly makes fascinating reading. If only it had Jim Bowen and the chance to gamble everything for a caravan or speedboat.

Extreme sports

The best of the best

Adrenalin Magazine **www.adrenalin-magazine.com**

The funky sound track, live video and action photography just scream 'Adrenalin' from the first page. No matter how you get your dose of excitement, you're bound to find something on this fresh and funky site. For more of the same but with the gloss and music turned off, take a look at Adventure Time (**www.adventuretime.com**)

The rest of the best

Extreme Sports **www.extremesports.com**

The bizarre navigation system on Extreme Sports somehow adds to the feeling of off-the-wall coolness which is just dripping from the site. Every conceivable extreme sport is covered through well-written features and some stunning photography – and, once you've finished with the adrenalin stuff, there are also plenty of entertainment reviews and features to help you relax.

■ *The best of the rest*

Aggressive Skating www.aggressive.com
Skating, with an angry face.

ESPN Sports espn.go.com/extreme
Very American, but full of action-packed news and features. Another masterpiece from the guys and gals at ESPN.

Ball games

Some ball games are more popular online than others. The following events may not be the most popular choices for UK net users, but we love 'em all.

■ *The best of the best*

The British Basketball League www.bbl.org.uk
An incredibly impressive basketballing resource which includes links to every single

club in the League, online ticket booking and even some well-stocked shopping. For more of the same, slam-dunk your way over to The English Basketball Association (**www.basketballengland.org.uk**).

The rest of the best

Baseball Stats	**www.stats.com**	NFL	**www.nfl.com**
NBA	**www.nba.com**	Superbowl	**www.superbowl.com**
Netball	**www.netball.org**		

Betting and gambling

The best of the best

Sporting Bet www.sportingbet.com

The first thing to know about Sporting Bet is that it's tax-free. No matter whether you live in the UK, Australia, the US or even Finland, you can place bets on some of the world's most high-profile sporting events, including basketball, hockey, soccer, cricket, motor sport, golf, horseracing, tennis and more.

The rest of the best

Blue Sq **www.bluesq.com**

Blue Sq(uare) is definitely one of the coolest online gambling sites, and it's not all sport either. Although you can place a bet on the usual array of sporting competitions, it's much more fun to bet on the plot of your favourite soap. The layout is extremely fresh and funky, and betting is as simple as you would expect.

Eurobet **www.eurobet.co.uk**

Betting giant Coral's foray into the world of e-commerce is predictably professional. Behind the uncluttered design lies an easy-to-use account application system allowing you to get up and running in no time, and if you want to know a little bit more before you place a bet, Coral has provided plenty of reassuring information about itself. A pretty safe bet.

Flutter **www.flutter.com**

Wanna bet? Then take a trip over to Flutter, where you can bet on anything you like against anyone you like. We bet you'll like it. We do.

Sports equipment shopping

The best of the best

Newitts **www.newitts.co.uk**

Newitts, the largest mail-order supplier of sporting goods in the UK, has been around since 1902 and, if its excellent site is anything to go by, it'll be around for a good few years yet. All of the thousands of products are available to order and, using a simple but very effective navigation system, it couldn't be easier to find what you're looking for.

The rest of the best

Complete Outdoors **www.complete-outdoors.co.uk**

The name says it all. Shoes, bags, tents, walking poles and everything else you might need to get back to nature, all at down-to-earth prices. The design is a little basic

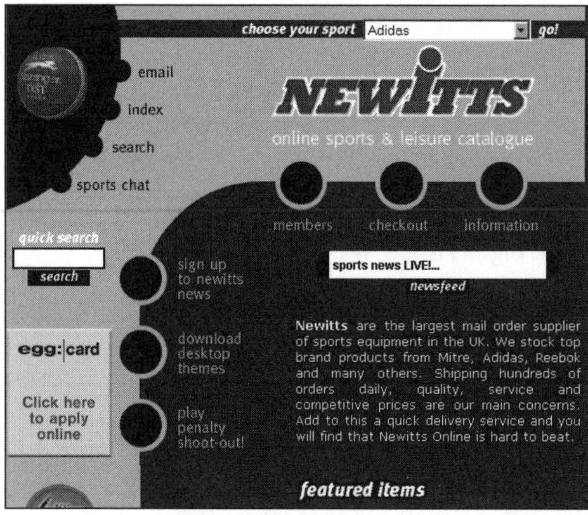

and some more pictures of the products would help, but if you know what you're looking for you shouldn't have too many problems.

Country Supplies **www.countrysupplies.com**

Over 10,000 products for the countryside enthusiast, including stuff for equestrian sports, fishing and shooting as well as a nice range of clothing and gifts. A superb site also boasting an events diary and resource centre.

Bid a Bike **www.bidabike.com**

Buying a bike is one thing, but bidding for one? It may take some getting used to, but specialist auction sites are growing in popularity. If you don't fancy the cut and thrust of the virtual auction room, you do have the option of using the more straightforward bike shopping section – but then again, where's the fun in that?

Legends Surf Shops **www.legends-surf-shops.co.uk**

If your idea of fun is standing on a plank of wood and getting wet, cold or bruised, then you'll certainly want to surf over to Legends. All types of boards are featured here, including surfboards and snowboards, and if you're feeling creative you can even build your own skateboard.

Fishing Warehouse **www.fishingwarehouse.co.uk**

More than just an online shop, Fishing Warehouse is a complete portal for fishing enthusiasts. The site includes some extremely well-written articles, plus a nice mix of news, reviews, forums and advice. Oh, and you can buy stuff, too.

Reel 'Em In **www.reelemin.co.uk**

Another great-looking fishing equipment store, this time featuring top angler Bob Church. Not quite as big as Fishing Warehouse yet, but well on its way.

Sportswear shopping

The best of the best

Blacks **www.blacks.co.uk**

Blacks is already famous for offering sports and outdoor wear on the high street but, like so many before it, it's decided to take a leap on to the web. Unlike many before it, however, it's actually done a very good job of it, offering a complete range of hiking shoes, rucksacks and related outdoor wear in an easy-to-browse format.

■ *The rest of the best*

Discount Sports **www.discountsports.co.uk**

No matter whether you're seriously sporty or just want to look cool in summer, Discount Sports will have something to suit you. Trainers, T-shirts and other sportswear with free delivery and – you've guessed it – discounted prices.

Kitbag **www.kitbag.com**

Kitbag started life by supplying replica football kits at internet prices but has since branched out into rugby, cricket and even Formula 1 clothing. Having been online for years, the company clearly knows how to sell on the web – ordering is a piece of cake and the after-sales service is not too shoddy either.

JD Sports **www.jdsports.co.uk**

You've seen it on the high street, now you can visit it online. As you'd expect, there's plenty of fashionable street and sportswear, including replica football kits and a good selection of trainers. Buying online could be easier and the prices aren't too amazing, but if you're nervous about shopping online, an established name like JD Sports is a good place to start.

9feet **www.9feet.com**

Not only does 9feet look extremely impressive, it also obviously knows its stuff. Claiming to be 'as into the outdoors as you are', the site provides clothing and accessories for mountain biking, adventure sports, hiking, walking, climbing, cycling and everything else you can think of.

24 hobbies and interests

The web is full of sites dedicated to every conceivable pastime, from stamp collecting to spot welding. It won't surprise you to hear that there's plenty more of the same in the Zingin Hobbies and Interests Guide (**www.zingin.com/guide/leisure/hobby**).

Home improvement

■ *The best of the best*

DIY Fixit **www.diyfixit.co.uk**
A wealth of UK-focused advice on all aspects of home improvement. Can you fix it? Yes, you can.

■ *The rest of the best*

Do It Yourself **www.doityourself.com**
Still looking? There's plenty more info on this large site.

Collecting

■ *The best of the best*

About Hobbies **www.about.com/hobbies**

About.com does it again with this great first stop for hobbyist information on the web.

■ *The rest of the best*

Suite101 **www.suite101.com**

One of the leading US community sites for collectors of anything and everything.

Collecting Channel **www.collectingchannel.com**

Hundreds of links to collecting sites from around the world.

25 gaming

It's probably fair to say that the internet has revolutionised computer gaming. Forget two-player gaming (I'll be joystick, you be keys) – online gaming allows you to compete with millions of players across the world. Even if you prefer to play alone, the latest hints, tips and cheats are always within easy reach.

Console and PC gaming

■ *The best of the best*

Games Domain **www.gamesdomain.co.uk**

Stuck on level 4? Unstick yourself with this fun-packed gaming site. Cheats and hints are available across all formats, including both console and PC titles – and there are plenty of up-to-date reviews to help you make the right choice.

■ *The rest of the best*

Game Zone **www.gamezone.com**
Plenty of stuff for the dedicated PC gamer, with information about the latest releases plus a veritable hard drive full of tips and cheats. Impressive stuff.

Dreamcast Lair **www.dreamcastlair.com**
Nice-looking site dedicated to all things Dreamcast, including product reviews, news and tons of cheats. For more of the same check out DC Guide (**www.dcguide.co.uk**).

Playpalace **www.playpalace.co.uk**
PlayStation owners rejoice. Playpalace features the usual blend of news, cheats and features, with a standard of presentation which can't fail to impress.

Online gaming

■ *The best of the best*

Gameplay **www.gameplay.com**
Gameplay has been around in different forms for ages, but has recently morphed

into something truly unique. Like a virtual game magazine, the site includes news, reviews, cheats and shopping, with some neat online gaming thrown in, too.

The rest of the best

BarrysWorld **www.barrysworld.com**
If you're looking for no-frills online gaming action, then look no further than this excellent service. Pretty much every popular game is featured and, if you're an experienced gamer, you'll feel instantly at home. Great stuff.

Yahoo! Games **games.yahoo.com**
Fancy a game of chess with a grand master in Russia or a few hands of bridge with someone in the next town? Then you'll definitely want to check out Yahoo! Games, which lets you compete at a number of popular games against players from across the globe. For more of the same, check out The MSN Gaming Zone (**www.zone.com**).

The Sony Station **www.station.sony.com**
Those generous folk at Sony allow you to play classics such as Trivial Pursuit and Wheel of Fortune with thousands of people around the world.

Games shopping

The best of the best

Games Street **www.gamesstreet.co.uk**
If you're new to internet shopping, you can buy here with confidence, knowing that this is one of the UK's largest online traders. OK, if you're looking for up-to-the-minute game news, cheats and big pictures of Lara Croft, you'll probably want to try somewhere else – but if you just want to buy games, it's hard to fault.

The rest of the best

Special Reserve **www.reserve.co.uk**
A definite contender for our 'how much information can you fit on the page at one time' award, Special Reserve has developed a site which is literally packed full of

games, hardware, reviews, cheats and other gamey stuff. For less than £7 a year you can join the Special Reserve Club, which will save you money on the already discounted prices. Special.

Games Paradise **www.gamesparadise.com**

Games Paradise is part of the WHSmith Online group, but still manages to retain some of its own individuality. The prices and range of products are no more outstanding than on other games sites, but the fact that it's supported by such a huge high street name makes it a safe bet for first-time buyers.

26 food and drink

A quick snack on the move, a meal for the kids, a cocktail after work, fast food, or a full gourmet feast – whatever you're hungry for, the internet makes it easy to arrange.

Food and drink portals

■ *The best of the best*

Taste **www.taste.co.uk**

A recipe finder, wine guides, news, reviews, features and even a section dedicated to the joys of chocolate – there's something for everyone, and the Carlton Food Network tie-in means that there are plenty of celebrity chefs on hand to provide

additional advice. If you don't fancy cooking then you'll also find plenty of restaurant information, food events and profiles of the world's top chefs – and you can buy all of your recipe books and kitchen gadgets in the secure online store.

The rest of the best

Epicurious **food.epicurious.com**

The usual menus, advice and features are all present and correct, but it's the other features which make the site such a joy to use: forums and chat rooms to swap ideas with your fellow gastronomes, mouth-watering food photography and the superb recipe file – a searchable database of over 11,000 recipes. All in all, if you love food – you'll adore Epicurious.

Food 'n' Drink **www.foodndrink.co.uk**

Not only does Food 'n' Drink laugh in the face of the word 'and', it's also one of the funkiest food sites on the web. Beyond the bright orange, split-screen front page, you'll find news, reviews, gossip, restaurant guides and, well, pretty much everything you'll find on the other food sites – but it's British, dammit.

Out of the Frying Pan **www.outofthefryingpan.com**

Well-written articles with an emphasis on fun, competitions, recipes, profiles of leading female chefs ('queens of cuisine'), kitchen gadgets and so much more make this an essential bookmark for foody females (and brave men). Think Delia Smith meets the Spice Girls.

BBC Food and Drink **www.bbc.co.uk/foodanddrink**

Jilly Goolden and Oz Clarke aside, there's plenty of menu advice, cunningly separated into starters, meat, fish, vegetarian, side dishes and desserts – and a nifty recipe finder to help you plan your next meal.

Foodlines **www.foodlines.com**

As with most of the food portals, the keystone here is the recipe archive, which is separated into an impressive number of easy-to-browse categories, making it extremely simple to find something suitable – from a light snack to a full gourmet feast. To complement the recipes, you'll also find healthy eating advice, an events listing, news, features and a wealth of resources for food lovers around the world.

About Home Cooking **homecooking.about.com**

We can always rely on our chums at About to provide a decent site, regardless of subject – and this one is no different. About's guide to Home Cooking features links, forums and recipes (surprise!), and is a great way to track down the best food resources the web has to offer.

CD Kitchen **www.cdkitchen.com**

Over 4,500 recipes, including some copies of famous brands (Kentucky Fried Chicken, Burger King Fries, etc.) plus a wealth of cooking tips, hints and links to the rest of the culinary web.

The Alternative to Food and Drink UK **www.alternative-food-and-drink.co.uk**

If you prefer your food in a pot, packet or can, you'll love The Alternative to Food and Drink UK, which offers an in-depth guide to everything from energy drinks to processed vegetarian food. Delia Smith probably wouldn't approve – but we definitely do.

The Kitchen Link **www.kitchenlink.com**

Looking for something that's not covered here? The Kitchen Link provides links to more than 10,000 food and drink sites on the web. Check out Chef Heaven (**www.chefheaven.com**) for more of the same.

Specialist portals

■ *The best of the best*

Chopstix **www.chopstix.co.uk**

A dedicated Chinese food portal, packed full of expert features, a daily recipe, and a veritable wok full of oriental goodness. Whether you just enjoy a chow mein or you're a professional chef, you'll find something to interest you – and by using the expert guide to Chinese cooking and ingredients, you can progress from the former to the latter in next to no time.

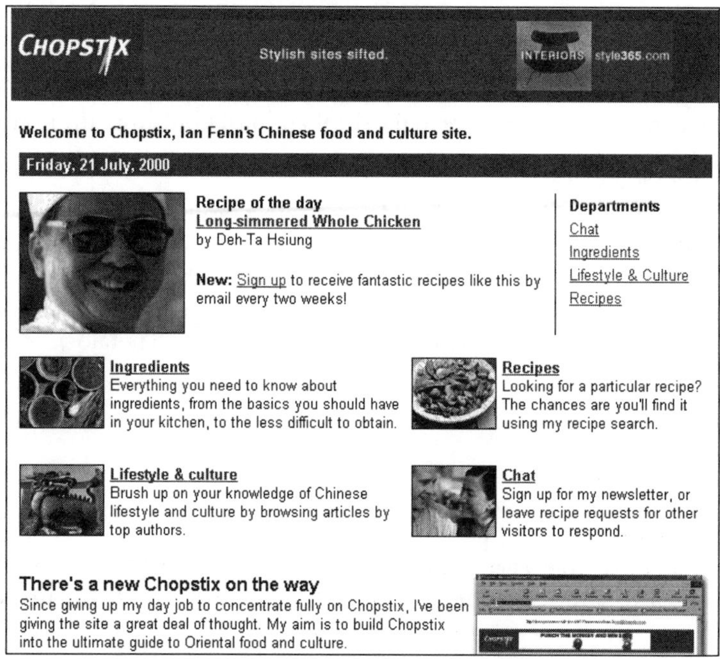

■ *The rest of the best*

Sanjeev Kapoor **www.sanjeevkapoor.com**

OK, it's confession time – we had no idea who Sanjeev Kapoor was until we discovered his excellent site. Apparently 'Master chef Sanjeev Kapoor is best known for his TV show *Khana Khazana*, a weekly programme on Zee TV' – so now you know. Confirming his celebrity status as the Gary Rhodes of Indian cuisine, Mr Kapoor has developed a suitably professional site which not only showcases his own creations but also allows visitors to post theirs.

Dr Gourmet **www.drgourmet.com**

Dr Gourmet is, in fact, Dr Timothy Harlan, who seems to be something of a health evangelist. Despite the off-puttingly healthy-sounding recipes, the food actually does look very nice, proving that there is a tasty alternative to pizza and chips.

Irish Food **www.irishfood.com**
The name says it all really. Recipes, restaurant reviews and links to ingredient suppliers and cookbooks make this a thoroughly enjoyable guide to Irish cuisine. Dig deeply though, there's much more to the site than you'd think from the front page.

Veg Web **www.vegweb.com**
The cluttered design of Veg Web should come with a health warning as it's likely to seriously damage your ability to navigate. The links are all over the place and there's little sign of a coherent menu system, but if you enjoy a challenge, there's plenty of excellent content to be found including a culinary dictionary, recipe exchange, e-mail newsletter and even vegetarian poetry (what rhymes with potato?).

Recipes

■ *The best of the best*

All Recipes **www.allrecipes.com**
You'll never suffer from chef's block again once you've visited this excellent site, which contains more recipes than we ever thought existed. All Recipes actually

consists of a number of specialist sites, focusing on different types of foods, including Chicken Recipe (www.chickenrecipe.com), Barbeque Recipe (www.barbequerecipe.com), Pasta Recipe (www.pastarecipe.com) and even the high-calorie Pie Recipe (www.pierecipe.com) – you can browse each site separately or search the whole lot by keyword. The recipes themselves are predictably excellent, with clear instructions so that even your average American can get stuck in – and the site looks great and is a breeze to navigate. Now, if only it had a Kebab Recipe site, life would be perfect.

The rest of the best

Recipe Center **www.recipecenter.com**

Even if you're not planning on doing any cooking, you'll find plenty here to whet your appetite (anyone had enough of the food puns yet?), with some excellent food photography, recipe forums and even a fact of the day – 'did you know that a tomato is actually a fruit?'. Well … yes, actually.

Recipe a Day **www.recipe-a-day.com**

Go on, have a wild stab in the dark, guess at what's on offer here. Yup, that's right – simply sign up using your e-mail address and they'll send you a new recipe every single day of the week.

Betty Crocker **www.bettycrocker.com**

America's answer to Mrs Beeton is one of the USA's most famous celebrity chefs. Her articles are published in hundreds of newspapers, she's a TV regular and her recipes are a benchmark for culinary quality. Now Betty's hit the web with this well-designed site with lots of recipes, practical advice and tips for reluctant cooks. It's glossy, it's *very* American and we love it.

Veggie Heaven **www.veggieheaven.com**

Over 230 meat-free recipes with easy-to-follow instructions and handy tips to keep you on the right track.

My Meals **www.my-meals.com**

Food sites seem to be obsessed with numbers. All of them boast how many recipes they contain – without any regard to the adage of quality over quantity. My Meals claims a respectable 10,000 dishes and, with its powerful search tool, it's easy enough to find the one you're after.

TuDocs **www.tudocs.com**

TuDocs – 'The Ultimate Directory of Cooking Sites' – is a recipe site plain and simple. No flashy design, no colour photographs or big-prize competitions, just a great range of food to suit all tastes and budgets, all graded for quality and taste.

The best of the rest

Good Cooking **www.goodcooking.com**

A useful, no-frills cooking resource, featuring the usual range of recipes and features in an easy-to-browse format. Well worth a look.

Meals for You **www.mealsforyou.com**

Huge food database site, making it easy to track down that elusive favourite recipe.

Top Secret Recipes **www.topsecretrecipes.com**

From McDonald's sweet and sour sauce to KFC's coleslaw, now you can recreate your favourite big-brand foods from the comfort of your own kitchen. For more of the same, try Copy Kat (**www.copykat.com**).

Edible Insects **www.eatbug.com**

Subtitled 'more than you ever wanted to know about eating bugs', this is certainly not one for the fussy eater. If, on the other hand, you fancy a quick meal (worm) or you want to impress the opposite sex with your culinary courage, then the recipes actually sound quite tempting. Having said that, with phrases like 'add ant larvae to taste', you're on your own with this one. Still got a craving for creepy crawlies? Try Nature Node (**www.naturenode.com/recipes/recipes_insects.html**).

Sticky Rice **www.stickyrice.com**

If you've yet to try sushi or you would like to know more about preparing it, the amusingly titled Sticky Rice site is a great place to start – with its selection of recipes, advice and everything else you need to start enjoying this surprisingly delicious delicacy.

For a complete guide to sites dealing with ingredients and popular food brands – plus a ton of other food and drink stuff – check out the Zingin Food & Drink Guide (**www.zingin.com/guide/leisure/food**).

Healthy eating and diet

The best of the best

Weight Watchers **uk.weightwatchers.com**

Weight Watchers may not have the glossiest site on the web but, by all accounts, its healthy eating and diet plans help thousands of people around the world lose weight every year. The site itself contains news, company details, e-mail information about your nearest meeting and even a forum to swap success stories.

The rest of the best

My Nutrition **www.mynutrition.co.uk**

News, a free nutrition consultation and expert advice all ensure that you're enjoying a balanced and nutritional diet. Weight Watchers is probably better for dedicated slimmers – but if you're trying to live a healthy life, My Nutrition will certainly set you off on the right track.

Weight Loss Resources **www.weightlossresources.co.uk**
An essential destination if you're serious about losing weight, WLR allows you to calculate your ideal target weight and offers a wealth of tools, advice and support to help you get there. It's not a free site, but you can try before you buy.

British Nutrition Foundation **www.nutrition.org.uk**
The official nature of the BNF site means you can be pretty sure that the information here is going to be accurate. Features dealing with issues as diverse as 'Chinese Healthy Eating' and 'Body Image & Eating Disorders', educational information and BNF news are all well-written and informative – but the really useful part is the list of links to relevant informative and educational sites. There are plenty of pictures of fruit, too.

dietsure.com **www.dietsure.com**
We can't vouch for the accuracy of the information here, but if it works as well as it seems to then dietsure.com is definitely worth checking out. In a nutshell, you type in information about your diet and lifestyle – either over a period of days or all at once – and the system sends you a full analysis via e-mail within a few hours. It's free and well worth a look.

Wine

■ *The best of the best*

WineToday **www.winetoday.com**
WineToday, from New York Times Digital, is unashamedly American in design and content – but there's still plenty for the UK visitor, including some very well-written reviews and advice which won't blind you with jargon. It's not all for enthusiastic amateurs though – there's a wealth of industry news and event listings, including dates and times of high-profile wine auctions, but the US angle means that it's not overly useful for anyone on this side of the Atlantic.

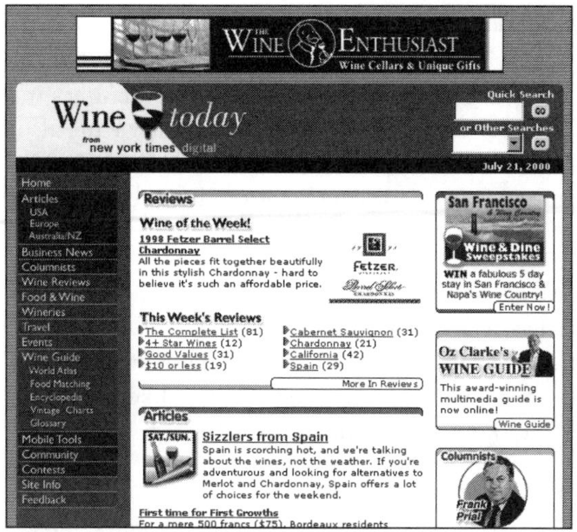

The rest of the best

Wine Spectator **www.winespectator.com**

Wine news, taste tests, cellar secrets, forums, travel information and more than two years' worth of archive material is available for free, the only downside being that, for the whole Wine Spectator experience, you'll have to pay.

Suite101 Wine **www.suite101.com/welcome.cfm/wines**

Like About (**www.about.com**), Suite101 offers a human-edited guide to websites, divided into hundreds of different subject categories. Its wine category is one of the best in the business, with featured articles, website reviews and a discussion forum allowing you to exchange views with fellow wine buffs. Splendid.

Wine Place **www.wineplace.nu**

A great example of content over design, containing everything you ever wanted to know about wine but were too busy drinking to ask. A guide to wine pronunciations should make it easier to order your favourite 'shatto nurf', and a rundown of some common words used to describe wines will make you an instant expert – and there's a whole lot more, including a forum and links to the best of the world *wine* web.

Wine Skinny **www.wineskinny.com**

Ever wondered what wine writers drink in their spare time? No, neither have we – but any idle curiosity is more than satisfied by Wine Skinny's imaginatively titled 'Weekend Wine' feature. The popular wine lifestyle magazine also features a whole host of entertaining features to give you the inside track on wine. We like. For a British perspective, try Andrew Jones's excellent Wine on the Web (**www.wineontheweb.co.uk**).

Wine.com **www.wine.com**

Wine.com is, above all else, an online shop, selling a huge variety of wines at more than reasonable prices. Why is that a problem? Well, for those of us who live outside the US, it's just too expensive and too much hassle to place an overseas order, meaning that we can look but we can't taste – like a child outside a closed sweetshop. Worth checking out for the features, though.

Grapevine Weekly **www.grapevineweekly.com**

Well-presented links to articles from some of the web's most impressive wine magazines. WineToday (see above) is featured along with The Wine News (**www.thewinenews.com**), Wine Pocket List (**www.winepocketlist.com**), Wine Brats (**www.winebrats.org**) and the wonderfully off-beat Wine X Wired (**www.winexwired.com**).

■ *The best of the rest*

Daily Wine **www.dailywine.com**

Fresh and funky site featuring a wine of the day, a wine of the month and a smattering of well-written features.

Wine Online **www.wineonline.co.uk**

In terms of design, Wine Online (which rhymes) doesn't really shine. However, there's a mixed bag of features, including news, information, event reviews and links to other interesting food and drink sites – some of which are well worth looking at. It's British, too!

Wine Links **www.winebreather.com/links.html**

If you've tried all of the above sites and you're still pining for wine then Wine Links will certainly quench your thirst. Also, be sure to check out the links to Scalextric-related sites at the bottom of the page. No, we're not sure why they're there either.

Don't forget to visit the Zingin Wine Guide (**www.zingin.com/guide/leisure/food/wine**) for a veritable cellar full of wine-related links.

Spirits and cocktails

The best of the best

iDrink **www.idrink.com**

Simply tell this superb site which ingredients you have at home – from apple juice to absinth – and it will suggest a range of cocktails that you can try. The database system looks simple enough but is, in fact, extremely fast and accurate, allowing you to search through thousands of recipes in seconds – and if your favourite isn't listed, you can make it available for other users to try.

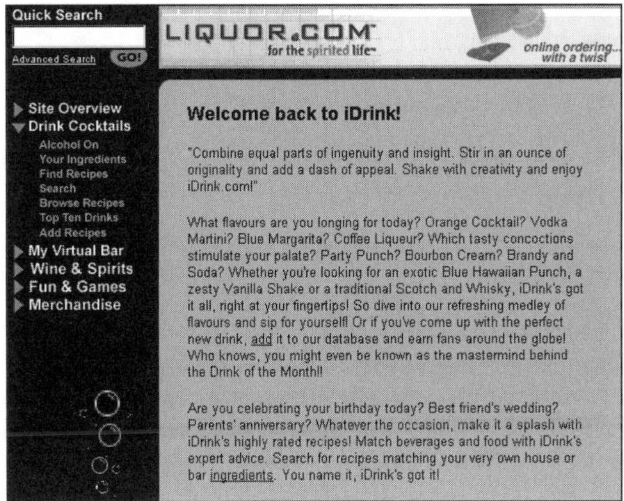

The rest of the best

Webtender **www.webtender.com**

Webtender – bartender, geddit? Never mind. This massive directory site provides a thorough guide to the best cocktail recipes, drink retailers and general-interest sites on the web. The design is not particularly inspiring – but if you want a quick way to find what you're looking for, it's hard to beat.

Cocktail Times **www.cocktailtimes.com**

This very nice-looking site features recipes, news, advice and information aplenty. Once you've finished testing out the recipes (in, say, five or six months) there's a whole world of other cocktail information, including the inside track on bartending, glassware, party planning and the history of cocktails. Nice.

Cocktail **hotwired.lycos.com/cocktail**

Proving that there's more to Lycos than searching for MP3s and pictures of Pamela Anderson, its excellent cocktail resource provides a drink of the week, well-stocked recipe archive, tips on mixing and the inspirational Virtual Blender which gives ideas on what to make next.

Cocktail.com **www.cocktail.com**

A slightly confusing mix of cocktail recipes, industry news and shopping. If you're heavily into the cocktail scene then you'll probably find plenty here, otherwise you're probably better off sticking to Cocktail Times or iDrink.

Beer

■ *The best of the best*

Breworld **www.breworld.com**

It's not often that the best site in a particular category hails from the UK – but in the case of the Staines-based Breworld, there really is no competition. Beer news, city guides, trade directories, discussion groups and, just in case you still can't find what you're looking for, more links than you can shake a pint at. So much beer, so little time.

■ *The rest of the best*

Beer Site **www.beersite.com**

Looking for beer sites? Look no further than the number one beer search site on the

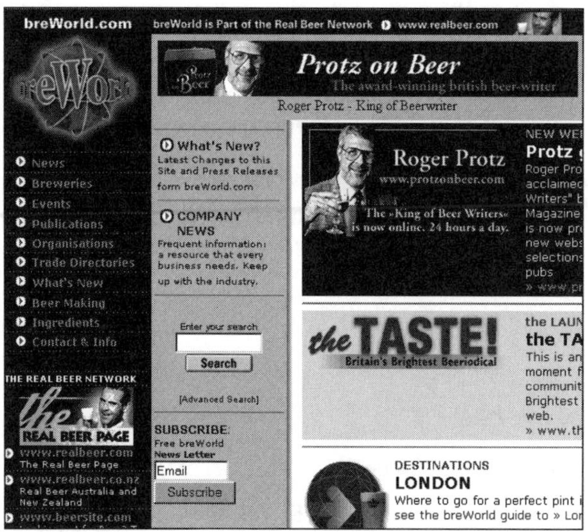

web – a kind of Yabroo!, if you will. From e-zines to official publications, it's all sorted, sifted and categorised for your browsing pleasure.

Beer **www.beer.com**

American site which proves that beer is more than just a drink, it's a way of life. Music, entertainment, live events, fun stuff and even the occasional mention of beer make this a pretty impressive way to waste a few hours.

Real Beer **www.realbeer.com**

Unashamedly American site claiming to offer everything you could ever want to know about beer, brewpubs, microbreweries, home brewing, and the beer industry. While that might not be quite true (unless you refuse to acknowledge anything outside the States), there's certainly lots to see and do.

The Campaign for Real Ale **www.camra.org.uk**

Fed up with bland chemical-filled beers? This could be your idea of heaven. For more of the same, try the Real Ale Guide (**www.real-ale-guide.co.uk**).

BarMeister **www.barmeister.com**

You might not think you need an 'online guide to drinking' – most people are pretty good at drinking without any help. However, this engaging site deals with everything other than the act itself, including drinking games, forums and cocktails.

Absolute Authority on Beer **www.absoluteauthority.com/beer**

This modestly titled affair features links to forums, mailing lists, advice and a whole load of other community-oriented stuff. Not exactly authoritative, but well worth a look nonetheless.

Soft drinks

■ *The best of the best*

Smell the Coffee **www.smellthecoffee.com**

The design may not be overly inspiring, but these people certainly know their coffee. Forums, well-written articles and an almost evangelical belief in the power of the coffee bean make this a thoroughly entertaining read.

The rest of the best

Tea Health www.teahealth.co.uk

This official site from the UK Tea Council (yes, there is a UK Tea Council) concentrates on the benefits of tea for a healthy lifestyle. There's even a nice photograph of a happy couple running across a beach, presumably after enjoying a nice cup of tea. For the main site check out Tea (**www.tea.co.uk**).

Koffee Korner www.koffeekorner.com

Kulture, health trivia, features, kartoons and enough koffee-related kontent to keep you kontent for a konsiderable amount of time. Less of the same at the Coffee Club (**www.coffee.co.uk**).

Tea Time www.teatime.com

Not as feature packed as Tea Health, but this useful resource is full of interesting tea facts and quotes – and there are regular chat sessions to discuss the finer points of the subject.

Tea and Coffee www.teaandcoffee.net

If you have a professional interest in the tea and coffee industries then this is an essential bookmark. Industry news, current affairs and features are the main ingredients, but there's also a message centre, calendar of events, up-to-the-minute information ticker and some sharp editorial content which will even appeal to non-industry types.

Restaurants, pubs and bars

The best of the best

AA Restaurant and Hotel Guide www.theaa.co.uk

Over 8,000 hotels and restaurants are featured in the comprehensive searchable guide to UK eateries. Simply choose the region, price band and quality of food you're looking for, and you'll instantly be offered a list of options – every one reviewed in detail by the AA. The presentation is spot on – and with the huge range of other features available on the site, it would be crazy not to visit at least once. Well done, the AA.

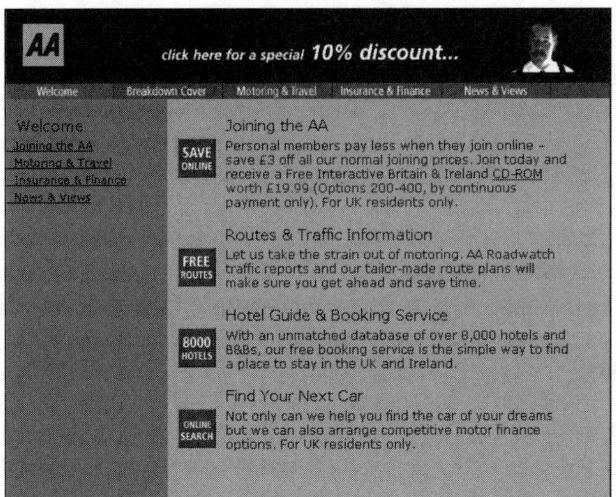

The rest of the best

Brewers & Licensed Retailers Association **www.blra.co.uk**

Pub locations, beer news and information, drink-driving advice (don't) and even taxation are covered on this superb resource – and, in the unlikely event that you can't find what you're looking for, there are plenty of links to external sites and resources.

Restaurants **www.restaurants.co.uk**

Another huge directory of restaurants across the UK, featuring brief details of over 20,000 establishments serving a wide variety of food. The listing is by no means complete – but then again, neither is the AA's – although the directory is expanding all the time and if your favourite isn't listed you can always add it yourself, if you don't mind paying £99 for the privilege.

The Good Pub Guide **www.goodpubs.co.uk**

The main purpose of this site is to persuade you to buy one of the company's *Good Guide* books – but even if you don't want to part with your money, there's plenty to see. The real crowd-puller is the (almost) complete database of the best British pubs, searchable by location, which is free to browse once you've registered as a visitor.

Pub World **www.pubworld.co.uk**

Pub World really does feature a whole world of pubs, including a huge searchable database of the UK's finest. Simply type in the town, style of pub or even the name, and you'll be presented with a list of possible matches. The site also boasts loads of other useful information for dedicated pubgoers.

Curry Pages **www.currypages.com**

If you like curry, you'll love Curry Pages, which lists thousands of Indian restaurants across the UK, including reviews by normal people who eat there regularly rather than overpaid food critics. Admittedly, this can make some of the reviews a little biased – but, by and large, it's a very reliable resource for spice fans. Also accessible via WAP. For more of the same, try Curry House (**www.curryhouse.co.uk**).

Top Table **www.toptable.co.uk**

Over 850 restaurants and venues are bookable from Top Table. Most of the establishments listed are based in the capital, as you might expect, but there are a few spread across Britain (and even a couple in Paris) if you look hard enough. Assuming you can find a restaurant near you, the booking system is excellent – and anecdotal evidence suggests that you can often get into 'unbookable' venues extremely easily.

■ *The best of the rest*

book2eat **www.book2eat.com**

More table-booking facilities from another slick site. As with Top Table, the majority of decent restaurants are in London – but if you do live in the capital, or are planning a visit, this could well be the easiest way to find a place to eat.

Speciality food shopping

■ *The best of the best*

SimplyOrganic Food Company **www.simplyorganic.net**

Over 1,500 organic products delivered directly to your home or office. There's fruit, veg, meat, wine, beer and so much more on offer and, when we shopped there, the service was first-rate. A great example of how online food shopping should be done.

■ *The rest of the best*

The Teddington Cheese Online **www.teddingtoncheese.co.uk**

Teddington Cheese may be a small company, but its no-frills site is capable of taking on all comers, with its huge range, stress-free ordering and refreshingly friendly service. How cheese would want to be sold.

Organics Direct **www.organicsdirect.com**

An award-winning and environmentally friendly site offering fruit, veg, pasta, baby food, bread, cakes and plenty more. Everything is certified organic (and GM-free), all of the growers are guaranteed a fair deal and the quality is second to none. Excellent.

The Fresh Food Co **www.freshfood.co.uk**

Claiming to be 'Britain's original, biggest and fastest online organic shopping service', the Fresh Food Co certainly has an impressive enough site. Everything is laid out in a sensible way, making it easy to browse – and the list of comments from satisfied customers should be more than enough to persuade you to start shopping.

Blue Mango **www.bluemango.co.uk**

Chutneys, confectionery, curds, dips and salsas, gifts, honey and sauces, jams, marmalades, mustards, flavoured sauces, teas and so much more make Blue Mango one of the most tempting stores on the web.

Clearwater Hampers **www.hamper.com**

If you prefer to buy your food by the basketful, then this is definitely the site for you. Some extremely tasty-sounding hampers are available here, packed with port, stilton, smoked salmon and other gourmet treats – and if you can't find exactly what you're looking for you can even create your own. For more of the same try 800 Hampers (**www.800hampers.com**).

French Hampers **www.frenchhampers.co.uk**

As the name suggests, this is a great place to find traditional French foods either as gifts or for your personal consumption. They're not cheap, with prices starting at £100 – and going up to £10,000 (!) – but the quality of food is excellent and the Which? Web Trader logo guarantees a stress-free ordering experience.

Fortnum and Mason **www.fortnumandmason.co.uk**

More hampers to be found here, plus a nice range of chocolates, wine and gifts. The site may be user-friendly but the prices are strictly for the well heeled.

Gourmet World **www.gourmet-world.co.uk**

From polentina cake to risotto, burgundy to claret, it's not cheap but it's mouth-wateringly tempting.

Sweet Mart **www.sweetmart.co.uk**

The Bristol Sweet Mart specialises in supplying ethnic foods and spices to the general public and to the restaurant trade – and, judging by the excellent range on its website, you shouldn't have too much trouble finding what you're looking for.

■ *The best of the rest*

Cyber Candy **www.cybercandy.co.uk**

Minimal design, maximum confection. Cyber Candy brings together a range of sweets from around the world including America, Australia, Japan, China and even New Zealand. Sweet.

Heinz Direct **www.heinz-direct.co.uk**

It may not be Fortnum and Mason, but Heinz has done well with this tins by mail service. The delivery can take up to a month – but if you don't mind waiting for your beans and baby food, it does the job.

Lobster **www.lobster.co.uk**

Caviar and champagne, fois gras and pastries – and, surprise surprise, there's even a range of hampers. If you enjoy your food and don't mind paying a few quid for the best, that's what you'll get here.

Drink shopping

■ *The best of the best*

ChateauOnline **www.chateauonline.co.uk**

Welcome to wine lovers' heaven. ChateauOnline combines an excellent range of

wine with expert advice from a top sommelier, so you can be sure that you're getting the best – and with bases in France, Germany and Ireland as well as the UK site you're certainly not dealing with a fly-by-night operation. If you're looking for a bottle of a particular rare vintage, check out Wine Searcher (**www.winesearcher.com**).

The rest of the best

Amivin **www.amivin.com**

If over 4,000 wines available for immediate delivery isn't enough to impress you, then the range of extra features offered by Amivin certainly will be. Wine buffs will be pleased at how easy it is to navigate straight to a particular vintage, but if you do need a little advice then Amivin's experts will be glad to point you in the right direction.

Now 365 **www.now365.com**

The usual range of beers, wines and spirits are here, along with a selection of soft drinks – and if you're worried about making sure your alcohol arrives safely, you'll be pleased to see the familiar Which? Web Trader logo.

Drinks Direct **www.drinks-direct.co.uk**
Uncluttered and simple to navigate, Drinks Direct will deliver your favourite tipple direct to your door within two working days – and while you're ordering, check out its range of flowers and chocolates, ideal for the special someone in your life.

Whisky Shop **www.whiskyshop.com**
Malts, rare, blended, liqueurs, half bottles and even miniatures (no more stealing from hotel mini-bars) ensure that no matter how much of which type of whisky you're after, you'll be spoilt for choice here.

Shopwine **www.shopwine.co.uk**
The name says it all. If you are shopping for wine you'll find an exceptional range on offer, categorised by style, country and price – while spirit lovers will definitely want to check out the site's Spirit Vault, which contains a superb range of brandies and malt whiskies as well as all the traditional favourites.

Supermarkets

■ *The best of the best*

Tesco **www.tesco.co.uk**
If you live within one of the growing number of Tesco delivery areas, then it's simply a case of registering online, choosing your items and waiting for a shiny delivery van to arrive with your weekly shopping. Naturally you are going to get situations where something you order isn't in stock, in which case you get the chance to opt for an alternative product. It's not just about food and drink, though – you can also buy books, music, gifts and even personal finance services. If this excellent service covered the whole of the UK there'd be no need to leave your house again. Well done, Tesco.

■ *The rest of the best*

Iceland **www.iceland.co.uk**
Mum may have gone to Iceland in an old advertising campaign – but now, thanks to Iceland's excellent home shopping service, she can stay home and put her feet up.

An impressive range of groceries is available for delivery to an impressive 97 per cent of the UK – and as long as you spend over £40, you won't pay any extra for the service.

Sainsbury's **www.sainsburys.co.uk**

Like Tesco, Sainsbury's home delivery service is only available to those lucky people who live in a restricted delivery area – but if you are fortunate enough to be eligible, you can call upon the services of a team of specially trained shoppers to do your shopping for you. The site itself is very well thought out, and there are some nice touches in the shopping system itself – such as allowing you to specify what size potatoes you want or how ripe you like your plums.

■ *The best of the rest*

Aldi	**www.aldi-stores.co.uk**	Co-op	**www.co-op.co.uk**
Asda	**www.asda.co.uk**	Safeway	**www.safeway.co.uk**
Budgens	**www.budgens.co.uk**	Waitrose	**www.waitrose.com**

comedy and fun stuff 27

The internet may be a goldmine of information and reference tools, but it's also a great place to unwind. From comedy to competitions, online games to offbeat time-wasters, there's certainly no shortage of entertaining content – if laughter really is the best medicine, the web is something of a miracle cure.

General comedy sites

■ *The best of the best*

Funny **www.funny.co.uk**

The UK's finest comedy database allows you to search for some of the funniest sites on the web. In addition to comedy news and features, the site's directory is

categorised into books, cartoons, comedians, computer humour, jokes, magazines, multimedia, one-liners, parody and a fair dose of weird stuff, making it easier than ever to find something to make you chuckle. Oh, and as it's a British site, most of the material is actually funny.

The rest of the best

Comedy Lounge **www.comedylounge.co.uk**

Profile of top comedians, a guide to the finest live comedy venues and a collection of features and links which will keep you laughing until you stop. Definitely one for the comedy connoisseur.

Ha Ha Bonk **www.hahabonk.com**

Calling this a portal would be like calling the Black Death a bit inconvenient – it's so much more than that, with video of some of the brightest stars in British comedy, plenty of offbeat and thoroughly entertaining content, festival and gig news, and a community section which allows you to 'chat, argue, abuse or share a joke with fellow comedy fans'. Splendid.

Humor Database **www.humordatabase.com**

Humor Database features thousands of jokes, each of them rated for content to avoid offending the youngsters. It may be a good idea in theory, but they might as well put up a little sign saying 'here's a rude one kids – make sure you read it'. There are some funny ones though. For more of the same, check out Jokes.com (**www.jokes.com**).

Comedy Online **www.comedyonline.co.uk**

If you're based in or around London, then Comedy Online may well be right up your street. In addition to the comprehensive listing of gigs, there are reviews, profiles, interviews and plenty of heated debate.

British TV Comedy **www.phill.co.uk**

Frighteningly comprehensive guide to the best of British Comedy, including episode guides and a database of stars.

Comedians and venues

The best of the best

Izzard www.izzard.com

All the official stuff is here, including tour dates, information from previous gigs and some interesting information about the man himself. But what makes this site really stand out is the additional content, which is pure Izzard genius.

The rest of the best

PythOnline www.pythonline.com

Despite not having done anything new for years (with good reason), Monty Python is still as popular as ever. Fans will be pleased to hear that the official site of Cleese, Palin, Idle, Chapman, Jones and Gilliam is just as bizarre as the timeless comedy itself. Discussions in the 'chit' room, the Spam Club and big flying angel baby things. Nuff said.

Chicago Comedy Festival	**www.comedytown.com**
Edinburgh Fringe	**www.edfringe.com**
Jongleurs	**www.jongleurs.com**
Melbourne Comedy Festival	**www.comedyfestival.com.au**
Montreal Comedy Festival	**www.hahaha.com**

Competitions and games

■ *The best of the best*

Jamba **www.jamba.co.uk**

This impressive site from Carlton offers some of the web's most enjoyable competitions and quizzes along with the opportunity to win big prizes, including CDs, electrical equipment and even some cold hard cash. Jamba is very similar to pub trivia machines, with the added excitement of competing against your fellow internet users as well as the clock – it's also completely free to play, saving you a small fortune in pound coins.

The rest of the best

Loquax **www.loquax.co.uk**

Every day on the web, there are thousands of opportunities to win big prizes. The trick is knowing where to find them – and knowing where to find them is what this rather nifty site does best. So next time you fancy a free trip to a Caribbean island or a bank account boost, head over to Loquax, find out there the action is and cross your fingers. Good luck.

Uproar **www.uproar.co.uk**

Featuring the ever exciting Family Fortunes game (which used to be on Jamba), Uproar is a must for competition fans who want that little bit of extra prize-winning action.

Football Manager **www.footballmanager.co.uk**

Play by mail seems amazingly outdated when you try your hand at online football management – decisions can be made instantly, the results are immediately visible and the sheer number of people online means that there can be some pretty substantial prize money on offer. Excellent.

The best of the rest

Banana Lotto **www.bananalotto.com**

A million quid up for grabs, without even paying a pound for a ticket. Can't say fairer than that.

Emode **www.emode.com**

Find out what breed of dog you are and which celebrity you are most compatible with by completing a range of quirky tests. Ticking boxes has never been so much fun. More of the same at 9 to 5 Cafe (**www.9to5cafe.com**).

Free Money **www.freemoney.fm**

Why bother with the hassle of quizzes and competitions when you can win a grand simply by answering a questionnaire?

Free Win **www.freewin.co.uk**

Win some fantastic prizes, every hour of every day.

E-zines

The best of the best

Salon www.salon.com

It may be American, but this daily online magazine boasts some of the finest editorial on the web. Lowbrow issues dealt with in a highbrow way, and vice versa.

The rest of the best

urban75 www.urban75.co.uk

Although urban75 aims itself squarely at anti-capitalist protesters and political activists, it still manages to be consistently entertaining regardless of where you stand.

Arts and Letters www.aldaily.com

A daily run-down of the most interesting and controversial writing on the web.

The Mighty Organ **www.themightyorgan.com**

It's a sad fact that we live in a constantly dumbed-down world, where sharp, entertaining journalism has been replaced by *Kenyon Confronts* and *Tonight With Trevor MacDonald*. So imagine our glee at finding the irreverent, yet thought provoking Mighty Organ. It even has an article about gnomes.

Spark Online **www.spark-online.com**

Great articles and extremely funky design make Spark an ideal way to waste a lunch break.

Weird and wonderful

■ *The best of the best*

The Onion **www.theonion.com**

This razor-sharp parody of tabloid journalism is one of the most (if not *the* most) visited comedy sites on the web. Unlike other sites which are happy to go for cheap, obvious laughs, The Onion excels through its intelligence and spot-on satirical observations which not only make you laugh out loud but will also change the way you look at journalism for ever.

The rest of the best

Joe Cartoon **www.joecartoon.com**

Those of a nervous disposition will probably want to avoid Joe Cartoon, which contains some of the most hilarious, but gory, interactive cartoons on the web. Our particular favourite is the Frog Blender. Great stuff.

TheSpark.com **www.thespark.com**

Home of the ever-popular Ask Jesus and the Fat Project. One of the few sites which manages to be both American and funny.

Media Pill **www.mediapill.com**

Movie stars, TV celebs and singers – no one is safe from this spoof round-up of the latest entertainment news which, like The Onion, you'll either love or hate. We love it. For an internet alternative, check out Satire Wire (**www.satirewire.com**), while true satire connoisseurs will definitely want to visit the online home of Private Eye (**www.private-eye.co.uk**).

Virtual Fishtank **www.virtualfishtank.com**

Build your own fish and take up fishkeeping without leaving your PC, thanks to the aquatic wonder that is Virtual Fishtank.

The Dialectizer **www.rinkworks.com/dialect**

If you're fed up with translating from English to French and German, why not try something different? A particular favourite is the English to Elmer Fudd translation – absolute poetry.

Irn Bru **www.irn-bru.co.uk**

The Irn Bru site is filled with downloads and gimmicks to wind up your friends and waste your workday. From mini-games to spoof e-mails, there's plenty to try out, our particular favourite being the automated robot chat thing that lets you chat to yourself for hours … and hours … and hours. Superb.

The Centre for the Easily Amused **www.amused.com**

Proficient in the art of wasting time at work? Take it to the next level with the shrine to slacking that is The Centre for the Easily Amused.

Brunching Shuttlecocks **www.brunching.com**

Never let it be said that we don't offer enough offbeat craziness to satisfy your satire lust. The Brunching Shuttlecocks indeed. Tsk.

Hollywood Stock Exchange **www.hsx.com**

Buying shares in major corporations is one thing, but how about investing in the success of Stephen Spielberg's latest movie or Tom Cruise's career? The Hollywood Stock Exchange allows you to buy shares in famous movie stars, Hollywood blockbusters, musicians and more – with all the excitement of more traditional share dealing.

Earth Cam **www.earthcam.com**

Make like Big Brother and see the world from the comfort of your computer with this huge collection of live cameras around the globe. From Big Ben to the Bahamas – it's all here.

Newgrounds **www.newgrounds.com**

Bump off Britney Spears, punch Puff Daddy, shoot the Spice Girls and hunt down Hanson. All in the worst possible taste.

Death Clock **www.deathclock.com**

Miserable? Depressed? Watching your life tick away? You ain't seen nothing yet. Definitely not for the faint-hearted.

I Hate Clowns **www.ihateclowns.com**

Stand up and declare your hatred for red-nosed, smiley entertainers – and play the ever popular 'Punch a Clown' game.

Kiss This Guy **www.kissthisguy.com**

Did you think it was 'Lucy in Disguise with Lions' instead of 'Lucy in the Sky with Diamonds'? Then this one's for you.

Answering Machine **www.answeringmachine.co.uk**

Forget dull answerphone messages, surf over to Answering Machine and download something far less boring.

Sissy Fight **www.sissyfight.com**

Relive playground bitchiness with this superbly entertaining site.

28 shopping

So far, we've featured online shops which specialise in everything from music to footwear, but we've barely scratched the surface of the products available on the internet. Shopping directories feature tens of thousands of stores offering a huge range of goods and services – more than you'll find on any high street – while specialist retailers combine expert product knowledge with the price and convenience associated with electronic shopping. So, if you haven't managed to find the shop you're looking for elsewhere in the book, you'll almost certainly find it here. Retail therapy has never been so much fun.

Shopping directories

■ *The best of the best*

Kelkoo **www.kelkoo.com**
Another site which proves that the best internet companies are the ones with the silly names (Google? Yahoo!?). Kelkoo is a truly global shop comparison site and, although some countries are better represented than others, over 25,000 merchants from around the world are listed. If you've got plenty of time on your hands you can browse the entire directory yourself, but it's much quicker to use the automated comparison system to sniff out the best price on books, music, films, games, computers, wine, electronics, toys, flights and a whole range of other stuff. Before you spend any money on the internet, make sure you shop around with this invaluable resource.

■ *The rest of the best*

2020 Shops **www.2020shops.com**
While Kelkoo is the online shopper's most powerful weapon, 2020 Shops is like a

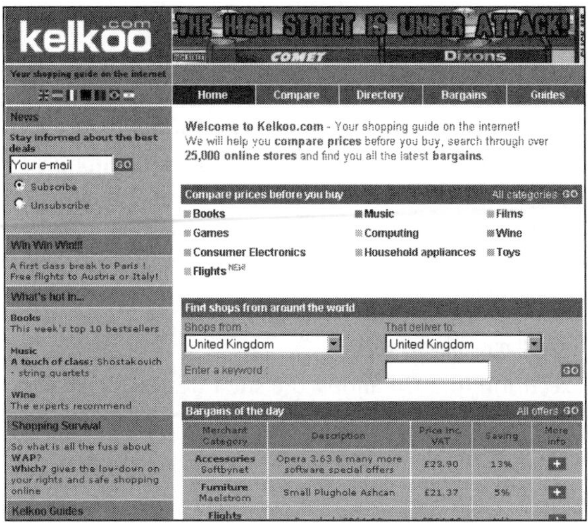

well-informed best mate. Other sites are busy developing automated shopping robots and search tools, but this directory is trying to give internet shopping a friendly face. What really makes 2020 Shops stand out from the crowd is not its huge range of features (there's a definite lack of gimmicks) but rather the quality of the site reviews, which have been written by professional journalists and are refreshingly honest and to the point. Whether you're buying a lamp or a lawnmower, a quick visit to this excellent site will get you on the right track in no time.

Shopsmart **www.shopsmart.com**

As one of the first UK sites to offer price comparison technology, Shopsmart has had plenty of time to get it right, so it's a piece of cake to find the best deal on books, DVDs, games, music and video. The only downside to Shopsmart's popularity is that it lacks the friendliness that makes sites like 2020 Shops so usable – but if you're into cold hard facts, it's hard to criticise.

Scan **www.scan.com**

Despite teething problems, Scan is a godsend for busy shoppers. Simply send a text message from your mobile phone telling it what you're looking for and, if you're happy with its quote, you can place an order instantly. Scantastic.

Ybag **www.ybag.com**

Taking a different approach to price comparison, Ybag makes the suppliers do the hard work so you don't have to. Once you've signed up for your free 'Ybag' you simply type in details of what you want to buy ('I want to buy a fridge for under £500') and it will send your request out to its network of suppliers via anonymous e-mail. If any of the suppliers think they have what you're looking for then they can send information directly to your Ybag for you to pick up at your convenience. If you're looking for business products and services, you'll find something similar at Mondus (**www.mondus.co.uk**).

Shops on the Net **www.shopsonthenet.com**

Very similar in execution to 2020 Shops, the site rates each shop out of 10 and also provides a mini-review and some essential information to point you in the right direction.

Buy **www.buy.co.uk**

Buy's goal is to take the hassle out of finding the best deal on services like gas, electricity, water and mobile phones, and it seems to be succeeding admirably. After you've answered a few very straightforward questions, you'll be given a list of suggested packages and tariffs from all the major suppliers. If you like what you see (and you probably will), you can simply click the 'buy' button to order online. Using the service is completely free and the advice is unbiased and very well informed.

■ *The best of the rest*

Blue Carrots **www.bluecarrots.com**

Crazy name, bright idea. Blue Carrots is a shopping directory with a difference, giving you cash back on everything you buy. Simply visit the site, sign up and start saving.

Hoojit **www.hoojit.com**

Hoojit may be the new kid on the shopping directory block, but if its innovative approach to price comparison is anything to go by, it is destined to get very big, very quickly.

My Taxi **www.mytaxi.co.uk**
Offering you 'more time to have fun', My Taxi combines a shopping directory with a range of well-written articles and features. Having said that, considering how long it's been around, the service could be better. Worth a look.

No Bags **www.nobags.com**
No Bags is clearly going for the youth vote with this fresh and funky site. Everything's covered here, from auctions to videos, and the content is more than acceptable. The potential is here for something very impressive, but at the moment it can't compete with the larger shopping directories.

Department stores and malls

■ *The best of the best*

Great Universal **www.greatuniversal.co.uk**
The online arm of Great Universal Stores doesn't fail to impress with this mammoth site. If you already have one of its paper catalogues you can use the online order form to speed things up, or if you're a first-time visitor it's simple enough to browse

through its incredible range of products. From nightwear to nit combs, boxer shorts to football kits, it's all here – and with years of mail order experience you can expect great customer service and prompt delivery. Proof that traditional companies can make a killing on the web.

The rest of the best

ShoppersUniverse.com **www.shoppersuniverse.com**

Another massive range of products and plenty of those slightly bizarre things you always see in catalogues – Elysée 10 Pad Exercise System, anyone? The prices are extremely competitive, and there's a handy gift finder so you can find the perfect microwave or set of spanners for the special person in your life.

Big Save **www.bigsave.com**

Books, hi-fi equipment, clothing, toys, gadgets, computers … the list goes on and on, and the prices are pretty competitive too. If you've got lots of shopping to do and not much time to do it, Big Save could well be the answer to your prayers.

Allders **www.allders.com**

Allders may not offer as many products online as in its high street stores, but you'll find a nice selection of furniture, electrical goods, gifts and clothing all wrapped up in a suitably stylish site. Also includes an excellent wedding gift service.

EshopOne **www.eshopone.co.uk**

Promising to offer quality products at internet prices, EshopOne is definitely catering for the higher end of the market with (among other things) hand-made greetings cards, Derwent crystal and a range of British meats.

Buckingham Gate **www.buckinghamgate.co.uk**

It feels expensive, it looks expensive and, you've guessed it, it is expensive. Buckingham Gate is the Harrods of online malls, with merchants such as Rolls-Royce, Clearwater Hampers, British Airways and Bentley.

The best of the rest

Argos **www.argos.co.uk**

If you have a copy of the Argos catalogue (who doesn't?) you can use the reference number to see if the product you want is available online – and, if not, there's enough here to choose an alternative. Brighter shopping.

Debenhams **www.debenhams.co.uk**

After a shaky start, Debenhams is starting to make some serious waves on the web with its slick-looking site and trademark range of fashion, flowers and gifts. OK, so there's nothing like the range here that you'll find on the high street – but if you don't mind sacrificing quantity for quality, you could do far worse.

doLondon **www.dolondon.com**

Now you can shop in the capital without leaving your computer, thanks to doLondon. Once you've found a virtual street – from Bond Street to Tottenham Court Road – it's a simple matter of clicking on a shop to start spending.

Marks & Spencer **www.marks-and-spencer.co.uk**

From school wear to financial services, Marks & Spencer is quickly transferring its huge range of products and services on to the web. The layout is uncluttered and the photography, especially in the food section, is enough to make your mouth water. Superb.

QVC **www.qvc.co.uk**

The UK's favourite home shopping channel hits the web with a continually expanding range of electrical goods, fashion, home and garden essentials. It's all very well designed and, if you're into gadgets, the site will have you tapping in your credit card number before you can say 'Wow, that's amazing … how much does it cost? And it's not available in the shops? I'll take twenty.'

Entertainment superstores

The best of the best

Amazon www.amazon.co.uk

Predictable? Perhaps, but despite its comfortable market position, Amazon continues to impress with its huge range and ultra-fast service. Books, videos, CDs and DVDs wrestle for shelf space, and the prices for best-selling items are up to 50 per cent off cover price. With the increasing popularity of price comparison sites, many online entertainment stores are being forced to cut prices to the bone to remain competitive – but when you've got everything you need in one place and service this good, there's often no need to go anywhere else.

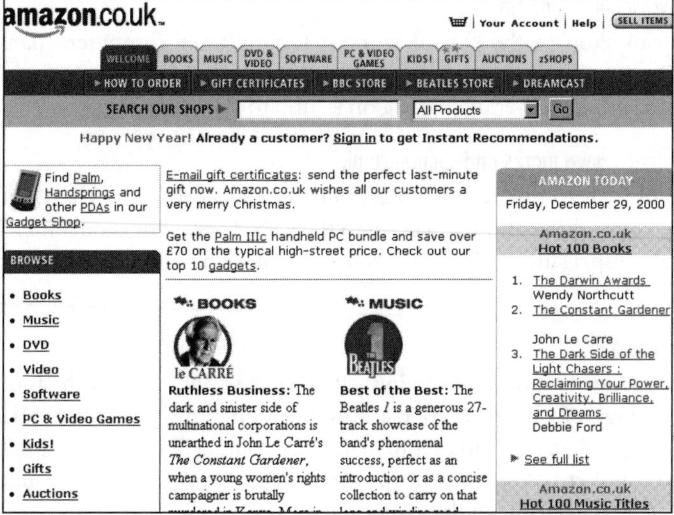

The rest of the best

Streets Online www.infront.co.uk

In the UK, only Streets Online comes anywhere near Amazon in terms of customer service and range of products. Rather than being a 'we sell everything' superstore,

Streets Online has set up individual shops to sell music, DVDs, games and books, all at extremely competitive prices and delivered in just a few days. In our experience, Amazon's delivery is that little bit quicker – but, if you don't mind waiting, you'll find everything you need without breaking the bank. Visit Audiostreet (**www.audiostreet.co.uk**) for music, Gamestreet (**www.gamesstreet.co.uk**) for games, Alphabet-street (**www.alphabetstreet.co.uk**) for books and DVDStreet (**www.dvdstreet.co.uk**) for … yup, you've guessed it.

Jungle **www.jungle.com**

Music, video, games and computer hardware are all available here at extremely competitive prices and, after a few teething problems, customer service is now up there with the best. One of the few companies (along with Streets Online) which could threaten Amazon's market share.

WHSmith Online **www.whsmith.co.uk**

Unlike some of its competitors, the high street's favourite newsagent and bookshop is obviously taking this whole internet thing very seriously indeed. As you'd expect, there are plenty of books (over 1.5 million in fact!), including the latest best sellers and some old favourites, but there's also a wide range of chart CDs, magazines, stationery, software, films and all of the other stuff you'd find in your local branch.

Electrical superstores

■ *The best of the best*

Unbeatable **www.unbeatable.co.uk**

They're not wrong, you know. Unbeatable's prices are generally much lower than you'll see elsewhere and there's a huge range of electrical equipment to choose from so you won't have any problems finding what you're looking for. Also, the presence of the Which? Web Trader logo means you can be confident that your order will arrive promptly and safely. First-class service from a first-class site.

■ *The rest of the best*

Comet **www.comet.co.uk**

This site from the high street favourite seems to have it all – a trusted name,

competitive prices, a huge range (over 2,000 products) and an extremely professional-looking site. If you're bargain hunting then you'll definitely want to shop around as you'll find better elsewhere – and Comet only guarantees to match prices found in other high street shops and not on the web. Having said that, if you'd rather pay a few pounds more to have that more peace of mind, you know where to come.

Quality Electrical Direct **www.qed-uk.com**

Claiming to offer the UK's largest range of electrical and gas appliances, this site certainly does have a massive range of TVs, videos, hi-fis, camcorders, cameras, fridges, freezers, cookers, washers, dryers and just about anything else you could possibly want.

21store.com **www.21store.com**

21store claims to 'know digital', and its site proves that it knows how to sell it too. Specialising in digital equipment and gadgets, it has a good range of palmtops, mobile phones, GPS systems – and its product descriptions are excellent. If you're into gadgets (or are a James Bond fan) this could well be your idea of heaven.

Easibuy.com **www.easibuy.com**

There's audio, video, garden equipment, kitchenware, cameras, vacuum cleaners, phones and so much more on this well-stocked but understated site. The prices on offer are usually considerably below high street prices, and a slick ordering system makes buying from the site ... erm ... easy.

Dixons **www.dixons.co.uk**

Considering that Dixons has changed the face of the internet with Freeserve you'd expect something pretty innovative from its electrical retail arm. Unfortunately, while there's nothing wrong with this site, there's certainly nothing outstanding either. All the usual products are present and correct, and the prices compare favourably with other high street retailers – it does the job but doesn't really impress.

■ *The best of the rest*

Battery Factory **www.batteryfactory.co.uk**

This electrical stuff is all well and good, but without batteries you won't get very far. For massive savings on power in all shapes and sizes, this is the site for you.

Hi-fi

■ *The best of the best*

Richer Sounds **www.richersounds.co.uk**

Richer regulars will be pleased to find that the Richer Sounds site is every bit as 'in your face' as its chain of shops. Anyone suffering from e-shopping safety paranoia will love the security measures in place here – not only is the order system located on a secure server, but the server itself is housed in an ex-MOD underground bunker. We kid you not.

■ *The rest of the best*

Hi-Fi Bitz **www.hifibitz.co.uk**

Hi-fi and home cinema separates are the name of the game here, with a very broad

selection of brands. The shopping system is not the most high-tech in the business, but it's simple enough to use – and as everything is backed up by the Which? Web Trader logo, you can buy with confidence.

Purley Radio   www.purleyradio.co.uk

No matter what type of wireless you're after, you'll find something to fit the bill at Purley, including the famous Trevor Baylis clockwork model as well as top brands like Sony, Grundig, Roberts and Bush.

Techtronics   www.techtronics.com

The design of this site may be a little unconventional, but the products available are nothing less than cutting edge. There are MP3 players, DVD, smart cards and some nifty home cinema stuff – and impatient shoppers will be pleased to hear that you can track your order online.

Blue Spot   www.bluespot.co.uk

In-car entertainment is not very well represented on the web, but if you don't mind restricting yourself to one brand (Blaupunkt) then Blue Spot is an excellent place to start. There are photographs of the entire range and an easy-to-use ordering system if you're tempted to spend some money – and with savings of up to 30 per cent on some models, that's a very definite possibility.

Mobile phones

■ *The best of the best*

The Carphone Warehouse **www.carphonewarehouse.co.uk**

One of the major benefits of buying from the Carphone Warehouse is the friendly, impartial advice – and it's obviously made a big effort to offer more of the same online. Simply answer a few questions about your budget, how often you plan to use the phone, and so on, and the site will suggest the right handset and tariff for you. If you like what you see (and you almost certainly will) then it only takes a couple of clicks to place your order. It looks great and works perfectly.

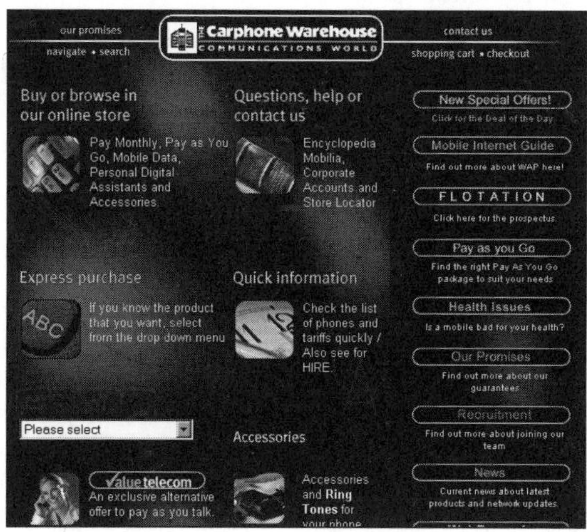

■ *The rest of the best*

Phone Factory **www.phonefactory.com**

Aimed squarely at the younger consumer, Phone Factory is a fun and friendly way to buy pre-pay mobiles. Beattie and her team of cute cartoon character chums act as guides to the site and are always happy to offer advice – even if you don't need it. When you've finished shopping there's a screen saver to download and an utterly pointless but strangely addictive card game thing to play.

Beyond 2000 **www.beyond-2000.co.uk**

There are no phones available here, just a massive array of accessories for just about any handset on the market – and the prices are among the best we've found. If you need a replacement aerial, an in-car charger or a cool leather case you'll find it all here.

■ *The best of the rest*

Although you'll rarely get the best deal by going direct to the mobile network operator, if you do want the peace of mind of dealing direct you'll definitely want to check out the following official sites.

BT Cellnet **www.btcellnet.co.uk**
One 2 One **www.one2one.co.uk**
Orange **www.orange.co.uk**
Virgin **www.virginmobile.com**
Vodafone **www.vodafone-retail.co.uk**

Clothing and fashion

■ *The best of the best*

Zoom **www.zoom.co.uk**

More than just a clothing store, this joint effort from the Arcadia Group stores (Topshop, Dorothy Perkins *et al.*) provides a wealth of lifestyle features as well as some pretty impressive online clothes shopping. The fact that the site is operated by such a recognisable name allows you to order with confidence, knowing that if it doesn't fit you shouldn't have too many problems getting things sorted.

■ *The rest of the best*

Kays **www.kaysnet.com**

Catalogue shoppers, this one's for you. The Kays catalogue is famous for providing stylish clothing at very reasonable prices – and its online version is no different. You can search by catalogue number or simply browse the easy-to-use online shop to choose your new wardrobe.

Haburi **www.haburi.com**

In a nutshell, Haburi offers branded clothing at factory outlet prices. The site excels in its range of casual wear, with most of the world's top brands making an appearance, sometimes at less than half the usual price. The layout of the site is uncluttered yet impressive, and ordering is straightforward enough – great if you want to be seen in designer clothes without paying designer prices.

Topman **www.topman.co.uk**

Like Zoom, Topman is trying very hard to be seen as a lifestyle magazine as well as a place to buy clothes. Music, dating, jokes and plenty of pictures of 'cooler than thou' models complement the online shopping system to make this a must-visit site for trendy folk.

Swerve **www.swerve.co.uk**

The design may not inspire you to whip out your credit card, but the prices probably will. Armani, Versace, Calvin Klein, D&G, Valentino, Diesel, Ralph Lauren, Timberland, Tommy Hilfiger, Yves St Laurent, Thomas Burberry, DKNY and the rest are all discounted, and Swerve even promises to beat any price found on another UK website.

Into Fashion **www.intofashion.com**

If you're the type of person who always looks at the label first, then Into Fashion could well be the site for you. The impressive-looking shop is full of T-shirts 'as worn by Zoe Ball' and trousers 'loved by Kate Moss', but behind all the name dropping there is actually a very user-friendly ordering system.

Fat Face **www.fatface.co.uk**

It may not be the UK's best-known brand, but when it comes to the web Fat Face is definitely at the top of the tree. Clear photography ensures that you know exactly what you're buying, and the ordering process couldn't be simpler. A British site that's one of the best in the world.

Novelty Togs **www.noveltytogs.com**

The best place to get hold of those South Park socks and Homer Simpson boxer shorts you've always wanted.

Skim.com **www.skim.com**

Who? Skim may not be the biggest name in fashion just yet, but we think it's destined for great things. Each item in the range comes with its very own unique Skim number plastered across the front, the idea being that if you see someone interesting wearing one, you can visit Skim.com and send them a message. OK, it's a bizarre idea and the clothes seem to be designed for very skinny people – but it's already huge in Zurich and, because you can order online, it won't be long before you start seeing Skim numbers on a street near you.

■ *The best of the rest*

AW Rust	**www.awrust.co.uk**	Diesel	**www.diesel.co.uk**
Best of British	**www.thebestofbritish.com**	Evans	**www.evans.ltd.uk**
Box Fresh	**www.boxfresh.co.uk**	Helly Hansen	**www.hellyhansen.com**
Bumps Maternity	**www.bumpsmaternity.com**	La Redoute	**www.redoute.co.uk**

Shoes and accessories

The best of the best

Shoe Shop **www.shoe-shop.com**

Europe's largest online shoe shop offers thousands of styles – all delivered free to anywhere in the UK. The prices on offer are already excellent – but if you do see anything cheaper elsewhere, make sure you let Shoe Shop know and it will refund the difference. In the unlikely event that Shoe Shop doesn't satisfy your footwear requirements, check out Shoe World (**www.shoeworld.com**) for links to a whole world of alternatives.

The rest of the best

The Jewellery Store **www.thejewellerystore.com**

Buying books on the web is one thing – but a wedding ring? Well, if you're prepared to take the plunge and spend some serious money online then this is a great place to do it. From necklaces to watches, there's an impressive range on offer at competitive prices and, if you're a nervous e-shopper, the Which? Webtrader logo should provide a little reassurance.

Figleaves.com **www.figleaves.com**

Both men and women are catered for here, with Brass Monkeys and Wonderbra among more than 70 brands on offer. The real winner here, though, is the well-thought-out range of extra services available to internet shoppers. If you need a bit of help choosing the right garment you can search just for bras, briefs or legwear, while secret romantics (and stalkers) will make good use of the 'Virtually anonymous' option.

Marcus Shoes **www.marcusshoes.com**

Sam Marcus has been delivering Loake shoes to London's office workers since 1975 – and with a client list which includes names such as ICI, the Bank of England, Rolls-Royce and Lloyd's of London, you can be pretty sure that the quality is top-notch. If you work in the City or Docklands, Sam will visit your office for a no-obligation fitting – and if you live further afield, the mail order service means you won't have to miss out.

Sea Glass Jewellery **www.seaglass.co.uk**

She sells sea shells on the sea shore. Well, no, she doesn't actually. If it's shiny and comes from the sea you'll find it made into some amazing jewellery here.

■ *The best of the rest*

Ann Summers **www.annsummers.co.uk**

Lingerie and so much more, designed for more daring tastes. Not one for the kiddies. For more of the same but with a higher price tag, check out Agent Provocateur (**www.agentprovocateur.com**).

Brief Look **www.brieflook.co.uk**

Another site in the Figleaves.com mould, Brief Look promises to take care of all your lingerie requirements. Nice range, and it looks good too.

CrueltyFreeShop.com **www.crueltyfreeshop.com**

Animal-friendly, ethical, vegan products delivered to your door, straight from the supplier. If you love animals, you'll love this.

Home design and improvement

■ *The best of the best*

Smarte **www.smarte.com**

A well-designed, one-stop shop allowing you to buy furniture, furnishings, DIY materials and services from a wide range of specialist designers, brand names and tradesmen. From rugs to roofers, it's all here.

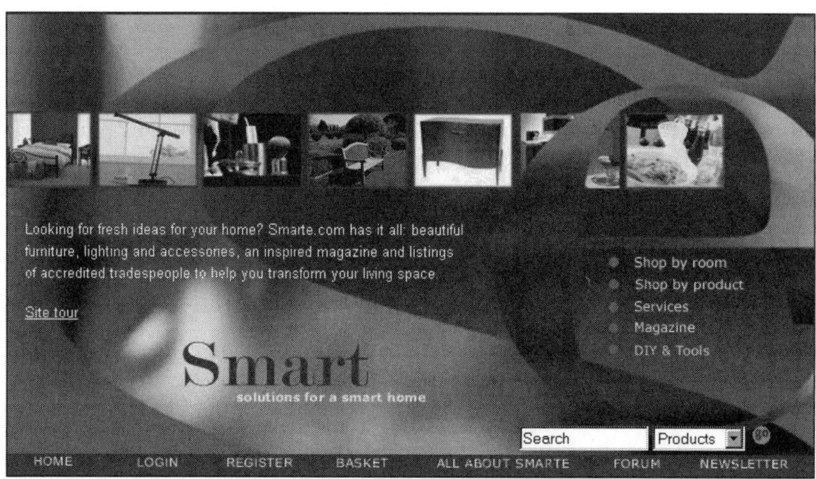

■ *The rest of the best*

Furniture Webstore **www.furniturewebstore.co.uk**

Specialising in beds, but with sofas and other stuff thrown in for good measure, Furniture Webstore claims to be able to deliver a quality divan bed almost anywhere in the UK in less than 48 hours – and even if time isn't a problem you'll find plenty to choose from. UK delivery is free and the site supports the Which? Web Trader code of practice, so you can sleep that little bit easier in your (new) bed.

Cooksons **www.cooksons.com**

Ready-made furniture is one thing – but if you really want to feel a sense of achievement, there's nothing like putting up a shelf or building a wall. Of course, you won't get too far without a decent set of tools and Cookson's has more than most – over 50,000 different hand and power tools are on offer, all at extremely reasonable prices.

Screwfix **www.screwfix.com**

A wealth of screws, nails, tools, sealants, adhesives, hardware, lighting and tons of other stuff to help improve your home. The prices are excellent and Screwfix promises next-day delivery if you order before 6 p.m.

Space2 **www.space2.com**

If you work from home, you'll love this ultra-stylish range of home office furniture – exclusively designed and sold by Space2. The award-winning desks and workstations are designed to allow you to work comfortably and are durable enough to withstand the rigours of life at home – but the great news is that, unlike its competitors, Space2 delivers within a couple of weeks so you can start working smarter almost straight away.

MFI **www.mfi.co.uk**

Bedrooms, kitchens and other little bits of self-assembly heaven make up this impressive-looking site from MFI. The range of furniture on offer could be a little better and, although there are a few special offers, the prices are pretty much what you'd expect in any of its Homeworks stores.

Good As It Looks **www.goodasitlooks.com**

A wide range of quality art prints and wallpaper to make your home look warm and inviting. Some useful advice too.

Pine Online **www.pineonline.co.uk**

Looking for quality furniture? Look no further than this nicely presented online shrine to pine. If you're unsure about buying on the web, make sure you check out the customer feedback section for a little reassurance.

Fun Light **www.funlight.co.uk**

If you're looking for home lighting ideas then a trip to Fun Light could well brighten your day. From flying rocket desk-lamps to illuminated water features, there's something here for everyone.

GE Lighting **www.gelighting.com/eu/home**
Work out the best way to light your home before you go out and buy bulbs. Hours of fun.

Web Blinds **www.web-blinds.com**
Don't get blinded by the sun – buy a new set of blinds from this truly slick site.

Gardening

The best of the best

Birstall **www.birstall.co.uk**
It's certainly not the sexiest-looking site on the web – but as online garden centres go, Birstall takes some beating. From seeds to shrubs via trowels and trees, the site is easily as well stocked as your local garden centre – and there's no need to drag the family around behind you.

The rest of the best

Dig It **www.dig-it.co.uk**

Dig It is one of the new breed of 'aren't plants cool' gardening sites which supply all of the usual gardening stuff but will also design and deliver a ready-made garden to your door – for a price. As for the question of whether gardening can ever be truly cool, Dig It seems pretty convinced. We blame Charlie Dimmock.

e-garden **www.e-garden.co.uk**

The main attraction of e-garden is the stable of celebrity writers who contribute to the site's excellent advice areas – but the shopping section is also well worth a look, with its selection of products and gardening books for beginners and professionals alike.

The best of the rest

Conservatories Online **www.conservatoriesonline.com**

Thinking of buying a conservatory? This portal site is designed for you – just don't throw any stones.

Indian Ocean **www.indian-ocean.co.uk**

Extremely well-designed site offering the largest selection of teak furniture on the web.

Cars

The best of the best

Autobytel **www.autobytel.co.uk**

The original and still the best. You can choose the type of car you're looking for, review your options and even place an order online. Works like a dream.

The rest of the best

Jam Jar **www.jamjar.com**

A chirpily titled site from Direct Line, offering a decent range of cars at pretty impressive prices. Well worth a look if you're allergic to slick salesmen.

Virgin Cars **www.virgincars.com**

Richard Branson does it again with this hip 'n' groovy virtual car showroom.

Car Price Check **www.carpricecheck.com**

After you've found your dream car online, make sure you drop by Car Price Check, which promises to try to beat whatever price you've been offered. Can't argue with that.

Toys and games

■ *The best of the best*

Early Learning Centre **www.elc.co.uk**

The site claims to be 'for moments money can't buy' – but if you're determined to try to spend something then it's extremely easy to do, due to the excellent range and the silky smooth ordering system. There's even order tracking to keep an eye on your toys' progress.

The rest of the best

Toys 'R' Us www.toysrus.co.uk
Following a recent redesign, Geoffrey and the gang are really starting to make some progress online. The design might not be anything special but, as it's quick to point out, Toys 'R' Us is backed by a chain of bricks and mortar stores so you can order in total confidence.

Hamleys www.hamleys.com
It may well be the world's finest toy shop in the real world, but on the internet Hamleys is not quite at the top of the tree. The site looks extremely professional, and finding particular items shouldn't cause you too many problems. Unfortunately, the site doesn't manage to achieve much fun and excitement so it's difficult to tell who Hamleys is targeting – with prices also in dollars, perhaps it's hoping for some sales from across the pond? All in all, it's a good way to shop from Hamleys, but not great if you're just doing some general toy shopping.

Gifts

The best of the best

Clare Florist www.clareflorist.co.uk
Saying it with flowers couldn't be simpler with this impressive site from the official florist to Edinburgh Castle. The themed arrangements are all illustrated with extremely clear photos, and forgetful romantics will be relieved to hear that if you order before 11 a.m. you can take advantage of same-day delivery. Clare Florist is one of those sites that we could rave about all day if you gave us the chance – but, to put it simply, if you're buying flowers this has to be your first stop. Blooming marvellous.

The rest of the best

Interflora www.interflora.co.uk
If you want to deliver flowers abroad then Interflora are the people to trust. With offices across the world from Algeria and Zambia, you won't have any problems

reaching friends and family wherever they happen to be – and Interflora's reputation means that you can be confident that the quality will be top-notch.

Thorntons **www.thorntons.co.uk**

You already know the Thorntons product range – chocolate, fudge, toffee and assorted chewy things. Its slightly cluttered site is a great way to send your loved one a few extra calories, and once you've spent a few minutes on the site you'll probably want to place an order for personal consumption as well.

Art Republic **www.artrepublic.com**

It's not strictly speaking a gift site – but if you're buying for an art lover, you'll find a wealth of ideas at Art Republic. There are quality prints and posters aplenty, and if you can't find the image you're looking for you can e-mail the experienced team who will be more than happy to help you out.

■ *The best of the rest*

Voucher Express **www.voucherexpress.co.uk**

Gift vouchers may be the easy way out of buying presents, but if you're not sure what they'd like then you can't go far wrong. All of the big names in UK retail and eating out are featured, including Our Price, PC World, Virgin, TGI Friday's and Victoria Wine, so you're bound to find something suitable – but do watch out for the somewhat steep postage charges.

Need a Present **www.needapresent.co.uk**
Slick-looking site offering a wide range of gifts for the gadget lover in your life. Failing that, buy some stuff for yourself. We like.

Card2Touch **www.card2touch.com**
This very impressive online greetings card store even allows you to personalise your card before you send it. A nice range at pretty painless prices.

Card Kingdom **www.cardkingdom.co.uk**
It may not be the slickest site on the web, but Card Kingdom offers a nice range of cards, wrapping paper, postcards and notelets – and the prices aren't bad either.

Balloon in a Box **www.ballooninabox.co.uk**
Show them you care with a balloon. In a box.

Gadgets

■ *The best of the best*

Firebox **www.firebox.com**
Make sure you set a spending limit before you visit Firebox, because once you've had a chance to browse its amazing range of gadgets, gizmos and assorted cool stuff you'll want to buy it all. Look out for the La-Z-Boy chair as seen on *Friends* and the ultra-nifty indoor helium airship.

■ *The rest of the best*

Boys Stuff **www.boysstuff.co.uk**
All the usual (and unusual) gadgets and gizmos are here, with a monthly run-down of the nine hottest products to give you some ideas – if you want to keep up with all the latest releases make sure you sign up for the site's free newsletter. Great stuff.

The Gadget Shop **www.thegadgetshop.co.uk**

Gadget Shop exclusives and old favourites are available for immediate (free) delivery, and the money-back guarantee gives you no reason to endure the unfathomable queuing system of its real-world stores.

asSeenonScreen **www.asseenonscreen.com**

Spend many happy hours buying the clothes, gadgets and assorted stuff that you've seen on your favourite TV programmes. From *Matrix*-type sunglasses to James Bond speedboats, it's all here.

Alt-Gifts **www.alt-gifts.com**

The Alternative Gift Company offers much more than just gadgets, with a wide range of imaginative present ideas which are just perfect for the person who has everything. If you can't find anything suitable from the huge range of products (which includes everything from Italian design and comedy soap), there are Alt-Gift experts on hand to help you out – and even electronic cards and a reminder service for when you've finished shopping.

Classified advertisements

The best of the best

Loot www.loot.com

Hundreds of thousands of adverts and tens of thousands of auctions make Loot one of the best places to get rid of your old stuff and buy a whole load of new stuff. Advertising on the site is free, and you can even access it using your WAP-enabled mobile phone – so you won't miss out on the bargains, no matter where you happen to be. Regular *Looters* will also want to grab a coffee in the virtual café, which provides a forum for sellers and buyers to exchange tips and tricks. Very nice.

The rest of the best

Exchange and Mart www.exchangeandmart.co.uk

Getting around *Exchange and Mart*'s online edition could be easier, but the sheer number of daily visitors to the site and the fact that your ad will appear in the paper version make it an essential destination, especially if you're selling your car. Placing an ad or contacting a seller is simple enough, and there's also a live auction if you like that sort of thing.

Autotrader **www.autotrader.co.uk**

New and used cars, insurance services, finance and even an impressive news section make it child's play to find your perfect vehicle here. For more of the same, try Fish4Cars (**www.fish4cars.co.uk**).

Preloved **www.preloved.co.uk**

Preloved may not be the first name that springs to mind when you think of classifieds, but this internet-only service is well designed, user-friendly and certainly worth checking out if you're looking for a bargain.

Auction sites

■ *The best of the best*

eBay **www.ebay.co.uk**

The UK branch of this huge global trading network is packed to the rafters with more items for sale than you can shake an auctioneer's hammer at. Putting an item

up for sale or making a bid only takes a few clicks, and eBay automatically insures you against fraud so you can buy with confidence – just don't get too carried away with the Beanie Babies and signed celebrity photos.

■ *The rest of the best*

QXL **www.qxl.com**

QXL is trying to position itself slightly more upmarket than the likes of eBay by offering online antique valuations and discounted hotel rooms. The whole affair is certainly much slicker than some of the others, but there are also fewer bargains to be had – if that's important to you. If you really want to bid on tickets, events and more exclusive items, you'll also want to check out the excellent Fired Up (**www.firedup.com**).

Yahoo! Auctions **uk.auctions.yahoo.com**

Packed with bargains, wonderfully cluttered and so very Yahoo!ish, this international auction site from the search giant features items from both the UK and abroad. If you want to stay within the UK, check out the small but perfectly formed eBid (**www.ebid.co.uk**).

Amazon Auctions **www.amazon.co.uk/auctions**

As you'd expect, Amazon's auction site has more than its fair share of books, music and film, including signed first editions, rare vinyl and all the *Star Wars* memorabilia you could ever want. There is, however, much more to it than that. The book giant has teamed up with Sotheby's (**sothebys.amazon.com**) to cater for those with more expensive tastes, and there are certainly some desirable lots to be had – if you're prepared to spend some serious money.

searching the web 29

So, you've made it this far through the book but you still haven't found the site you need – what are the chances of that?! Well, pretty large actually – there are literally billions of pages of information online, and there just aren't enough trees in the world to allow us to list them all in one book. The only downside to having the world's biggest library at your fingertips is the absence of the world's biggest librarian to sort the gems from the junk. However, despite the ever expanding nature of the web, it's still quite straightforward to track down what you're after if you know where to look, which is where this section comes in – and don't forget to flip to the front of the book for our guide to stress-free searching.

General global search tools

■ *The best of the best*

Google **www.google.com**

If we were stranded on a desert island and could only choose one search engine, then this would be it. Although Google is a relative newcomer compared to some of the old favourites, its highly intelligent search method has taken it straight to the top of the tree for both ease of use and quality of results. In terms of coverage, although it can't claim to know everything, this search monster is capable of searching over 1 billion individual web pages (1,326,920,000 at the time of writing) so you're bound to find something of interest and, if you don't, there are links to the other main search engines at the bottom of each result page.

■ *The rest of the best*

Yahoo! **www.yahoo.com**

Because real human beings build its directory, you'd expect something pretty special

from Yahoo! – just imagine a directory without any broken links or poor-quality sites! Unfortunately, due to the massive number of new sites coming on to the web and old ones disappearing, Yahoo!'s surfers are unable to keep up and, as a result, the directory is full of broken links and some very strong adult content. Having said that, if you try Google and don't find anything suitable (and you don't mind wading through broken links) then Yahoo! is an old favourite that's still well worth trying.

AltaVista **www.altavista.com**

Gimmick lovers rejoice! AltaVista has more toys – sorry, features – than you can shake a virtual stick at but, unlike some of its competitors, still manages to remain pretty easy to use. If you're new to the world of searching and want some extra advice, AltaVista provides a useful 'cheat sheet' to get you started, and there are more tips displayed beneath the search box itself.

AltaVista also has a UK site (see the next section on General UK Search Tools), but if you're interested in sites outside the UK and USA, try sticking the code for that country on the end of the address: for example, if you're looking specifically for Dutch or Swedish information, try **www.altavista.nl** or **www.altavista.se**. The range of features on these different national sites does vary, but some of them are very nifty indeed!

Hotbot **www.hotbot.com**

While Hotbot's database may not be as large as the likes of AltaVista or Northern Light (see below), it's certainly the easiest site to use for complex searches. Using a very straightforward set of tick-boxes and drop-down menus, you can tell the search engine to look for exact phrases, certain keywords, links to a particular page, people's names and much more – you can even ask just for pages which contain music or video.

Northern Light **www.northernlight.com**

Although it isn't as well known as the likes of Yahoo!, mainly because it doesn't spend billions on advertising, Northern Light is capable of searching a massive number of pages and usually returns some excellent results. Admittedly, the layout of the site leaves a lot to be desired and the bizarre system of sorting results into little folders may put you off initially (you can just ignore them!), but these aren't major problems and certainly shouldn't stop you from trying it out.

The best of the rest

Euroseek **www.euroseek.com**

Just when you were beginning to think that, on the web at least, the word 'international' could be substituted for 'American', along comes a dedicated European search tool. Or at least, that's what it claims. Euroseek does allow you to search in any one of over 40 languages and the results produced are usually pretty accurate – so if you're looking for foreign language material, this could well come up trumps.

Excite **www.excite.com**

Although Excite is an extremely powerful search tool, its global search site produces a large number of American results. Its UK version (**www.excite.co.uk**), however, is excellent and full details can be found in the General UK Search Tools section which follows.

General UK search tools

■ *The best of the best*

UK Plus **www.ukplus.co.uk**

More than just a web directory, UK Plus offers news, features and dedicated sections for Scotland, Ireland and Wales. When it comes to searching (or browsing) for UK sites, the directory produces some excellent results although, naturally, you won't find anything like the number you'd get on the international sites.

■ *The rest of the best*

Excite UK **www.excite.co.uk**

While many of the American search engines are happy to stick *.co.uk* at the end of their name and claim to have produced a UK version, Excite is really making an effort to produce something different. Yes, you'll still find a whole load of US information, but there are also plenty of British sites and the balance is about right if you choose the right keywords.

250000 **www.250000.co.uk**

The real attraction of this directory is the fact that it's sorted by region, so you can look for sites based in your neck of the woods, whether you live in Aberdeen or Wrexham – although, as you'd expect, the big cities have more listings than some of the smaller towns.

Search Engine.com **www.searchengine.com**

Formerly SearchUK, Search Engine.com is like UK Plus but without the news and features. Like UK Plus, you'll find plenty of UK-specific results using either a standard search box or by browsing categories which include Business, Careers & Employment, Computers & Internet, Education, Entertainment, Environment, Health, Kids, Leisure and Money.

Ask Jeeves **www.ask.co.uk**

Ask Jeeves was one of the first search engines to allow complete sentences rather than just keywords, and, as sites of this type go, it's pretty good at its job. The design looks great, but we can't help feeling that the English butler character must work better for American visitors (**www.ask.com**) than over here. And as for phrases like 'may one have your feedback?' – oh dear.

AltaVista UK **www.altavista.co.uk**

Like Excite, AltaVista is making a real effort to appeal to UK users both with the quality of its content (news, weather, polls, etc.) and also a fair number of .co.uk addresses in the search results. If you're familiar with the American version of AltaVista then you'll be pleased to find the same features on the UK site, including the ability to search for different media types and the family filter to keep the youngsters safe. Splendid.

Mirago **www.mirago.co.uk**

So many words, so little page space. Mirago seems determined to pack as much text on its front page as humanly possible and, as a result, loses some points in the usability stakes. Fortunately, there's also plenty to see and do on Mirago, with news, TV listings, tutorials and, of course, a search engine which was one of the first in the UK to allow you to filter adult material.

The best of the rest

Infoseek	**www.infoseek.co.uk**	Lycos	**www.lycos.co.uk**
Looksmart	**www.looksmart.co.uk**	Yahoo!	**www.yahoo.co.uk**

Metasearch tools

The best of the best

MetaCrawler **www.metacrawler.com**

It's always pleasant to see an American site which takes UK surfers seriously, and MetaCrawler certainly seems to realise that there is life on this side of the Atlantic, allowing you to either search the whole web or stick to UK sites. Your keywords are sent to such search giants as Google, Infoseek and Excite and, if you feel like it, you can even restrict the results to MP3 files, images, newsgroups, auction items and directory categories.

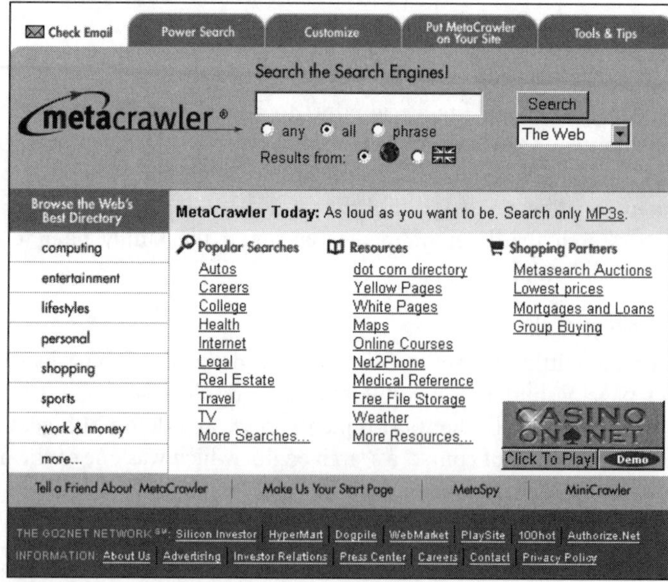

The best of the rest

ixquick **www.ixquick.com**
Whether or not it's the world's most powerful metasearch engine as it claims to be, ixquick is certainly up there with the best of them. All of the big search engines and directories are covered – and you can even search for MP3s, news and pictures, if you're into that sort of thing.

Dogpile **www.dogpile.com**
Another close contender for best of breed (excuse the pun), Dogpile differs from MetaCrawler in a number of ways. Firstly, if a particular search site doesn't produce any results, Dogpile will tell you (e.g. 'Excite produced 0 results') so you at least know where *not* to try future searches on that subject – very useful if you're using a metasearch as a starting point for a number of searches. Secondly, the site only has a US version, so if you're only after UK sites you'll need to look elsewhere.

General expert guides

The best of the best

About **www.about.com**
The original expert guide site, About has been around for years and offers a massive amount of information on almost every conceivable subject. Each of the subjects (from Art to Zoology) is maintained by an expert guide who also provides articles and general advice, as well as moderating discussion forums and generally helping out where needed. There's even a little picture of your guide in the top corner of each section, giving the site a very friendly feel.

The rest of the best

The Open Directory Project **www.dmoz.org**
Rather than attempting to keep track of the huge growth of the web on its own, Netscape launched the Open Directory Project, which relies on thousands of enthusiastic amateur volunteers to browse the web and add sites to the database. The idea is simple enough, but it works extremely well – with a higher standard of

links than some of the automated sites, and brief descriptions of the sites to keep you on the right track.

All Experts **www.allexperts.com**

Another American site, this time offering question-and-answer-style advice on a range of subjects from auto repairs to UFO sightings. Thousands of expert guides are standing by to take your questions so, whatever you've always been dying to ask, you'll find the answers here.

Young people's search resources

■ *The best of the best*

Yahooligans! **www.yahooligans.com**

In case the name doesn't give it away, this is Yahoo!'s attempt at attracting future web addicts with fun, games and a huge directory of child-friendly sites. The design is suitably bright and over the top – although it might well give adults a headache – and the links are chunky enough to be used by even the youngest web surfers. The sites listed have all been reviewed by human search guides to ensure that no dodgy

material slips through but, as there isn't a UK version yet, you might still want to give younger kids a hand when using it to prevent them getting utterly confused by the American spelling and talk of US national holidays.

■ *The rest of the best*

Ask Jeeves for Kids **www.ajkids.com**

Another tool which seems convinced that children love sites which look like they've been designed by three-year-olds (perhaps they do), Ask Jeeves for Kids allows children to search using real questions rather than just keywords.

Business directories

■ *The best of the best*

Scoot **www.scoot.co.uk**

Scoot also exists as a telephone enquiry service, but it's on the web that it really excels. Using this superb resource couldn't be easier – simply type in the kind of company you are looking for and where you'd like it to be based, and Scoot will present you with a list of businesses and services, ranked according to how near to you they are. Once you've found the company you need, you can use the contact details provided to get in touch or, if you prefer, you can fax them, visit their site, call up a street map or even send them a text message – all completely free of charge. Superb.

The rest of the best

Yell **www.yell.co.uk**

As you'd expect, Yellow Pages has been quick to establish itself on the web to avoid losing business to young upstarts like Scoot. Yell, as it likes to be called online, offers the usual search options – by name, service or location – in a surprisingly bright setting. The database is just as comprehensive as you'd expect from good old Yellow Pages, and with cinema, property, shopping, travel and weather info there's more than enough to keep you busy.

Ask Alex **www.askalex.co.uk**

If Scoot and Yell don't produce any decent results, there are two possibilities – either there are no horse whisperers in Leeds or you need to look elsewhere. Although you may not have heard of Ask Alex, if you've ever looked for a business on the web then the chances are you've used a version of it as it provides search results to Freeserve, Dun & Bradstreet, VirginBiz.net and even the Department of Trade and Industry.

■ *The best of the rest*

County Web **www.countyweb.co.uk**

This site covers 2.1 million businesses, separated into regional portals, which is nifty enough on its own, but when you also consider the other services offered by County Web you can't fail to be impressed. News, sport, places of interest, local police, property, jobs, cars, events, horoscopes and much more are available both on its website and on your mobile phone via WAP – and the design is not too shoddy either.

Fish4 **www.fish4.co.uk**

Very similar in operation to Scoot in that you can search by name, location or type and are provided with a detailed map to help you get there. The difference here is that with all the extra features available, you'll probably have no need to leave the house anyway.

Thom Web **www.thomweb.co.uk**

The official Thomson Directory site doesn't seem to have its act quite as together as Yell and Scoot. Yes, all of the directory search features are there, and if you don't find what you're looking for elsewhere then it's worth a try – but the design is a little uninspiring and most of the extra features (web and people searches, etc.) are actually offered by partners rather than Thom Web, so you may as well just use your favourite search engine or portal.

Reference tools

■ *The best of the best*

Britannica **www.britannica.com**

The online version of Britain's favourite encyclopaedia is certainly an impressive affair. Not only will you find the entire contents of the encyclopaedia, searchable by

category and keyword, but there are also expert articles on a range of topical issues, a guide to the best of the web (sounds familiar!), international news stories and even a shop.

The rest of the best

Encarta **www.encarta.com**

Encarta started life as a CD-ROM encyclopaedia from the mighty Microsoft but has since evolved into something of a reference monster. Over 16,000 articles are available, representing less than half of the entire database – if you want the rest you'll have to pay – but there's also a dictionary, atlas and plenty of other Microsoft-sponsored content to make up for the shortfall.

The Virtual Reference Desk **www.refdesk.com**

If you don't fancy the idea of ploughing through loads of reference sites, then a quick visit to this simple but effective site, which allows you to search eight popular sources at once, could well be the answer.

Dictionary **www.dictionary.com**

Simple but very effective, Dictionary will instantly check the spelling and definition of any word you throw at it. To be honest, that's about as far as most people will use the site – but if you do stick around a bit longer, there are plenty of other bits, including tips on usage and style, discussion forums, foreign dictionaries and even a word of the day. Of course, if you're not happy with the word of the day, you can substitute it for another one on the equally excellent Thesaurus (**www.thesaurus.com**).

Ask A Librarian **www.earl.org.uk/ask**

As if librarians weren't busy enough already, they've now generously given up their time to help internet users track down elusive pieces of information. Using the service is very simple, and very free: you simply type in your question, click the send button and within two working days you'll get an answer. But the best bit is you can talk as loudly as you like while you type your question without the risk of anyone telling you to 'shhhhhhh'.

■ *The best of the rest*

Encyclopedia.com **www.encyclopedia.com**

Inspired name, inspiring content. Not the best of the bunch, but a great way to find extra back-up information.

Boxmind.com **www.boxmind.com**

Still looking? Check out the complete directory of online reference tools at **www.boxmind.com**.

E-mail addresses

■ *The best of the best*

Yahoo! People Search **people.yahoo.com**

The only real difference between the various e-mail search sites is the number of people in their database. Other than that, they all allow you to search by name, city and state (ahem) and offer complementary features such as address books, maps, phone number look-ups and everything else you need to become a fully fledged stalker. Due to the sheer number of people who use Yahoo! (many of them also using Yahoo!'s free e-mail service) you can expect a fair number of results here – although, again, you're more likely to find 10,000 US citizens for every European. Worth a try though, eh?

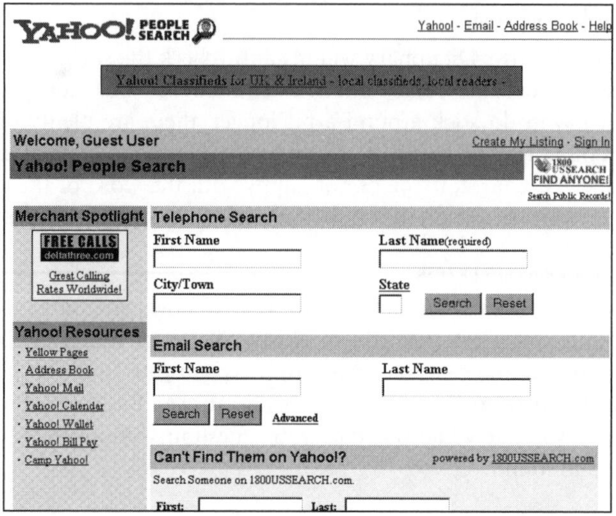

The best of the rest

Infospace UK **www.infospaceuk.com**

Not the largest of databases, but this UK-specific site does at least know where Bedfordshire is. If Yahoo! lets you down then you might have more luck here.

Bigfoot **www.bigfoot.com**

It's big and it has plenty of pictures of feet – but there's more to Bigfoot than just a stupid name. The site offers a people finder (naturally), a web search facility and free e-mail – but it still assumes you'll want to search by state!

Whowhere (Lycos) **www.whowhere.com**

Like Yahoo!, Lycos has millions of visitors passing through its virtual doors every day, so there's a good chance it knows how to get hold of a few of them. When you've tried – and quite possibly failed – to find the person you need, there are plenty of impressive features to get rid of some of the disappointment including, somewhat bizarrely, an ancestor search.

Internet Address Finder **www.iaf.net**

If you've got this far down the list, it's probably starting to look a bit desperate. Don't give up hope yet though, as there are over six and a half million people listed on the IAF. One of the nice features here is the fact that you can search by domain (e.g. *@zingin.com*) or organisation (e.g. *Zingin*), meaning that, in the case of business addresses, you might find one of the colleagues of the person you're looking for, who can point you in the right direction.

Switch Board **www.switchboard.com**

OK, now you can give up.

Phone numbers and addresses

■ *The best of the best*

BT Phonenet **www.bt.co.uk/phonenetuk**

In a nutshell, this is the entire BT phone book, searchable by name, address and

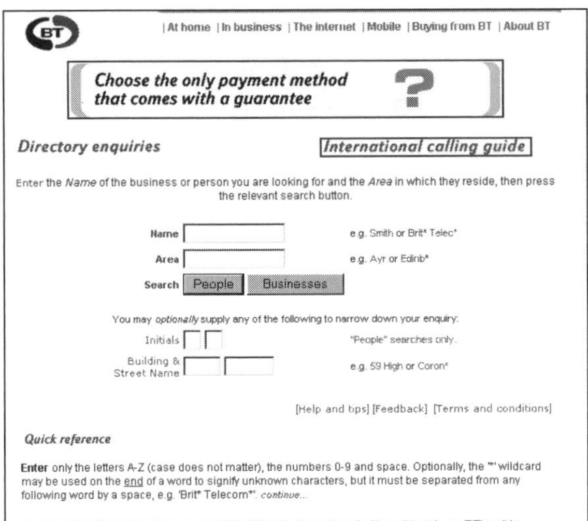

region. Obviously you won't find any ex-directory details here, but if you're looking for a business, or a non-secretive person, then this easy-to-use, free site does everything it should with the minimum of frills and fuss.

■ *The rest of the best*

192.com **www.192.com**

In theory 192 is better than BT Phonenet as it also contains some ex-directory information. Unfortunately, however, unlike BT, you have to pay extra to carry out unlimited searches and, although it doesn't cost a fortune, it still seems a bit unfair when the others manage to do it for nothing.

Discussion groups

■ *The best of the best*

Forum One **www.forumone.com**

Not all discussion groups are part of Usenet. There are plenty of independent web-based forums which allow users to post messages on all manner of subjects. To find

a forum that's your cup of tea, it's well worth checking out Forum One, which claims to list more than 300,000 of them!

■ *The best of the rest*

Supernews **www.supernews.com**

If you like your newsgroups to be free of junk mail then you're going to have to pay for the privilege. Supernews has been in the Usenet business for a long time and certainly offers a reliable way of getting connected but, unlike Deja News, it ain't free – although there's a free 30-day trial if you want to try before you buy. Another good (paid) option is Easy Usenet (**www.easyusenet.com**).

Forté, Inc **www.forteinc.com**

If your ISP gives you access to Usenet but you'd like a little more control over your posts than Outlook Express allows, you'll want to download a dedicated news reader – and there's none better than Free Agent (free) or Agent (not free) from Forté.

Chinwag **www.chinwag.com**

Chinwag may not offer a huge range of discussion groups, but some, like its UK Netmarketing group, are considered to be among the best in the world. Well worth a look if you're into the business side of the web, or stand-up comedy.

Liszts Usenet Directory **www.liszts.com/news**

So you've got access to Usenet and want to know what's available? You'll find a complete run-down here. Simple as that really.

Mailing lists

■ *The best of the best*

Liszts **www.liszts.com**

If you want to get involved with an e-mail discussion list, you'll find more than 90,000 of them here. Either browse by category or do a quick search for something that interests you, send an e-mail to the owner of the list asking to join, and in a few minutes you'll be up and running. For more instantaneous discussion, Liszts also has a directory of chat servers which is well worth a look.

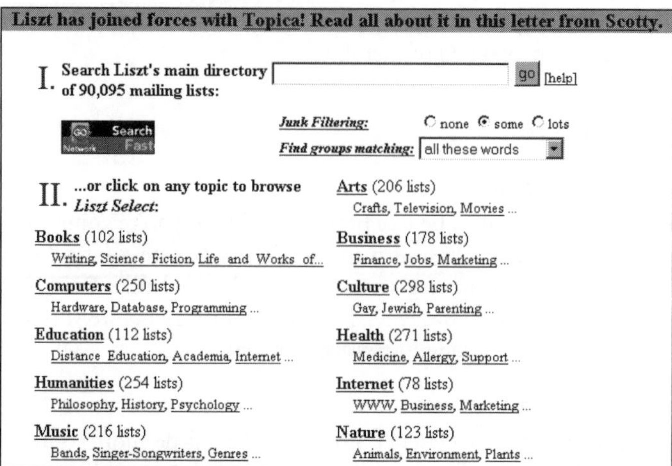

The rest of the best

Yahoo! Groups **www.groups.yahoo.com**

eGroups provides the tools to allow anyone to set up their own e-mail discussion group. If you fancy starting a group, it won't cost you a penny and will only take a few moments but, until you get the hang of things, you'll probably just want to check out the thousands of existing ones. An easy-to-use community-building resource, where everybody knows your name.

Free Pint **www.freepint.co.uk**

Anyone who regularly searches the internet for business- or research-related sites has got to subscribe to Free Pint. Not only will you receive a monthly newsletter filled with search tips and tricks but you'll also get access to the Free Pint bar, a web-based forum to ask questions and exchange answers as well as a wealth of industry news, book reviews and a whole host of free stuff. Rude not to really.

Finally, don't forget to subscribe to the free Zingin e-mail newsletter by visiting **www.zingin.com/daily**.

information on the move (WAP) 30

The internet is great if you happen to be within easy reach of a computer. Although internet cafés have become extremely widespread, there are still times when it would be nice to be able to use the web on the move. The answer, of course, is Wireless Application Protocol or WAP, which allows you to view the internet (or at least a cut-down version of it) on your mobile phone. The number of WAP sites is still pretty limited and if you want the full-blown multimedia experience of the web then you're still going to have to rely on an internet café or laptop, but, if you can cope with no-frills browsing, the following recommended search and directory sites will lead you to the best of the mobile internet.

■ *The best of the best*

Google **wap.google.com**

Already our search engine of choice, Google was the first search engine to really 'get'

Google Search

Google How to Google

Home About Google

Google WAP Search

Go mobile with industry's first comprehensive wireless search engine

Related Links

Press release

How to access

Google is the first search engine to bring the entire World Wide Web to mobile devices with a beta version of its award-winning search engine optimized for WAP phones.

Users of WAP phones can now search the web with the same unprecedented levels of ease and accuracy as users of Google's award-winning desktop-based search engine. Fewer than 1 percent of websites are published in Wireless Markup Language (WML). Google's WAP search translates the rest of the web from HTML to WML on the fly, enabling users without desktop access to find and view any website using Google and a WAP-enabled mobile phone.

Unique Features

Take advantage of Google's industry leading features including:

Size: Search more than 500 million web pages instead of the very limited number of WML pages.

Speed: Enjoy quick-loading results pages.

WAP. Not only can you access its entire database of sites (not just the WAP ones), but if you click on a link to a non-WAP site, Google will translate the page for viewing on your mobile. Bringing the entire web to your mobile phone – another master-stroke.

The rest of the best

Awooga **www.awooga.com**

It's fresh, it's funky and it's got a stupid name, but it's also one of the UK's most comprehensive guides to the wireless internet. In addition to a well-stocked directory, you'll find WAP-related news, downloads, books, advice and features to keep you up to date with this fast-moving technology.

2Thumbs Wap **www.2thumbswap.com**

Another silly name, another great source of WAP links, news, products and discussion forums. Both this and Awooga should be essential bookmarks for any dedicated mobile surfer.

Yahoo! Mobile UK **uk.mobile.yahoo.com**

It comes as no major surprise that Yahoo! has jumped on the WAP bandwagon with this feature-packed but not overly comprehensive directory. Well worth a look if Awooga and 2Thumbs Wap draw a blank – and knowing Yahoo!, it will grow quickly.

WAPaw **www.wapaw.com**

Another impressive WAP directory that seems to contain quite a few sites missed by the others.

No particular place to go?

Surfing the web is fast replacing television as the boredom reliever of choice in houses across the world, and for good reason – there's loads to see and do and it's more interactive than staring at a flickering box in the corner of the room. The only difference is that TV doesn't require any effort, you can simply slump on the sofa, switch it on (not necessarily in that order) and aimlessly flick through the channels until you find something interesting. Or snooker.

On the web, unless you actively look for something you won't find it – which explains why at this very moment there are millions of people around the world staring blankly at their computer screens, typing random words into search engines to see if something interesting comes up. We've all done it.

So is there a way to stop this madness? Yup, simply look in on some of the internet's popular web guides which offer suggestions for cool sites of the day, weird sites of the day, popular sites of the week and a whole load of other starting points for your internet adventure.

Cool Site of the Day **www.coolsiteoftheday.com**

The site which started it all is still churning out a daily piece of online coolness to millions of web surfers around the world. The quality of sites varies wildly, but there's enough here to waste hours and hours and hours.

Hot 100 **www.hot100.com**
The week's 100 most visited websites. If they're good enough for everyone else...

The Netmag **www.thenetmag.co.uk**
The UK's most popular internet magazine offers its recommendations for the best sites on the web.

Web 100 **www.web100.com**
The 100 best sites in a wide variety of categories.

Don't forget to check our daily pick of the best of the web at Zingin.com (**www.zingin.com**). You know you want to.

Still looking?

Although we've tried to cover the most useful and interesting sites on the web we're not infallible (hard to believe but true!).

If you can't find the information you're looking for, why not visit us online? At Zingin.com (**www.zingin.com**) you'll find all the links listed here plus an up-to-date directory of the best new sites, tools and resources.

Don't panic if you're still having no luck, just check our Search Guide (**www.zingin.com/guide/search**), where our team of human search experts will try their hardest to help you out – and it won't cost you a penny!

quick reference guide

1 News and weather

The Australian	www.news.com.au	4
BBC Online	www.bbc.co.uk/news	2
CNN (USA)	www.cnn.com	4
Electronic Telegraph	www.electronictelegraph.co.uk	3
El País (Spain)	www.elpais.es	4
Fish 4	www.fish4.co.uk	2
Guardian Unlimited	www.guardianunlimited.co.uk	2
Independent	www.independent.co.uk	3
Irish Times	www.irish-times.com	4
Keep Ahead	www.keepahead.com	2
Le Monde (France)	www.lemonde.fr	4
The Met Office	www.met-office.gov.uk	4
Mirror	www.mirror.co.uk	4
Moreover	www.moreover.com	2
Newsnow	www.newsnow.co.uk	1
The Paperboy	www.thepaperboy.com	2
Reuters (Global)	www.reuters.com/news	4
Sky	www.sky.com	3
Sun	www.thesun.co.uk	4
Teletext	www.teletext.co.uk	3
Times	www.the-times.co.uk	4
The Weather Underground	www.wunderground.com	4
Yahoo! Weather	weather.yahoo.com	5

2 Money

AA Insurance	www.aainsurance.co.uk	20
Accounting Web TaxZONE	www.accountingweb.co.uk/tax	31
American Express	www.americanexpress.co.uk	16
Altodigital	www.altodigital.com	29
Armchair Millionaire	www.armchairmillionaire.com	23
Bank of England	www.bankofengland.co.uk	30
Barclaycard	www.barclaycard.co.uk	16
Barclays	www.barclays.co.uk	13
Barclays Stockbrokers	www.barclays-stockbrokers.com	25
Blays	www.blays.co.uk	10
Bloomberg UK	www.bloomberg.co.uk	7
BUPA	www.bupa.co.uk	20
Business Advice Online	www.businessadviceonline.org	28
Buy	www.buy.co.uk	11
Cahoot	www.cahoot.com	13
Carpetbaggers	www.carpetbaggers.co.uk	11
CGU Direct	www.cgu-direct.co.uk	19
Charcol Online	www.charcolonline.co.uk	18
Charles Schwab	www.schwab-worldwide.com/Europe	24
Chartered Institute of Taxation	www.tax.org.uk	31
Check Your Bank	www.checkyourbank.com	11
Children's Money World	www.childrensmoneyworld.com	9
Citibank	www.citibank.com	13

3 Home buying

4 Employment

5 Law and public information

6 Computers and technology

7 Communication

8 Travel

9 Relationships and marriage

10 Parenting

11 Health

12 Education

13 Lifestyle

14 Family advice

15 Genealogy

16 Pets and animals

17 Entertainment news

18 Music and radio

19 Film

20 Television

21 Live entertainment

22 Books, culture and the arts

23 Sport

24 Hobbies and interests

25 Gaming

26 Food and drink

27 Comedy and fun stuff

28 Shopping

29 Searching the web

Google	www.google.com	285
Hotbot	www.hotbot.com	287
Infoseek	www.infoseek.co.uk	290
Infospace UK	www.infospaceuk.com	298
Internet Address Finder	www.iaf.net	299
ixquick	www.ixquick.com	291
Liszts	www.liszts.com	301
Liszts Usenet Directory	www.liszts.com/news	301
Looksmart	www.looksmart.co.uk	290
Lycos	www.lycos.co.uk	290
MetaCrawler	www.metacrawler.com	290
Mirago	www.mirago.co.uk	289
Northern Light	www.northernlight.com	287
The Open Directory Project	www.dmoz.org	291
Scoot	www.scoot.co.uk	293
Search Engine.com	www.searchengine.com	289
Supernews	www.supernews.com	301
Switch Board	www.switchboard.com	299
Thesaurus	www.thesaurus.com	297
Thom Web	www.thomweb.co.uk	295
UK Plus	www.ukplus.co.uk	288
Yahoo!	www.yahoo.com	285
Yahooligans!	www.yahooligans.com	292
Yahoo! People Search	people.yahoo.com	297
Yell	www.yell.co.uk	294
The Virtual Reference Desk	www.refdesk.com	296
Whowhere (Lycos)	www.whowhere.com	298
Yahoo! Groups	www.groups.yahoo.com	000

30 Information on the move (WAP)

2Thumbs Wap	www.2thumbswap.com	304
Awooga	www.awooga.com	304
Google	wap.google.com	303
WAPaw	www.wapaw.com	304
Yahoo! Mobile UK	uk.mobile.yahoo.com	304

No particular place to go?

Cool Site of the Day	www.coolsiteoftheday.com	305
Hot 100	www.hot100.com	306
The Netmag	www.thenetmag.co.uk	306
Web 100	www.web100.com	306

Zingin links

E-mail	www.zingin.com/mail
Feedback (e-mail)	feedback@zingin.com
Feedback (form)	www.zingin.com/feedback.html
Home	www.zingin.com
Mistakes and modifications	oops@zingin.com
Net Events Diary	www.zingin.com/diary
Newsletter	www.zingin.com/daily
Search Guide	www.zingin.com/guide/info/search
Suggest a Site	www.zingin.com/add.html